P9-ECT-334

YOUNG MARINER MELVILLE

Young Mariner Melville

by JEAN GOULD

ILLUSTRATED BY DONALD McKAY

DODD, MEAD & COMPANY
New York : 1956

Library of Congress Catalog Card Number: 56-10917

Printed in the United States of America
by Vail-Ballou Press, Inc., Binghamton, N. Y.

CONTENTS

YOUNG MARINER MELVILLE

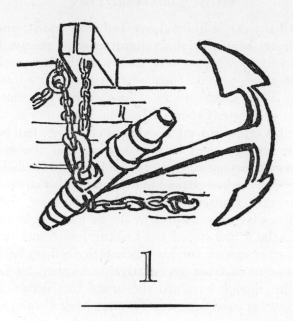

1

THE YOUNG MARINER GOES TO SEA

HIS NAME was Herman Melville—and he was setting out to sea.

He had left the little village of Lansingburgh in upstate New York only a day or two before with his brother Allan, bidding his mother, four sisters and small brother a fond and cheery good-by. But inside he was not a little quavery at the thought of going to sea, leaving his family and the peaceful village on the Hudson for the unknown roughness of a sailor's life aboard ship. He was excited, it was true, with the singing excitement of a poetic imagination creating fresh visions of his new career as the river boat from Albany carried him closer and closer to it; and his young heart beat with an exultant sense of release from the pinched, genteel poverty of his mother's household, of the straining to make ends meet, begging a few hundred dollars from Uncle Peter Gansevoort, his mother's brother, or Uncle Thomas Melville, his father's.

Since his father's death six years before, life had been a constant struggle, and he was hoping that the months ahead would change all that. He had worked in his Uncle Peter's bank; he had clerked in the cap and fur store of his older brother, Gansevoort Melville—a business that had failed when Gansevoort became ill; he had taught school, but the school had closed for lack of funds, and he was only another mouth for his mother to feed on bank accounts borrowed from one relative or another. So he had turned his thoughts toward the broad blue ocean. After all, two of his cousins, young Thomas Melville and Guert Gansevoort, were sailors and both of them had successful careers. Why shouldn't he? And why shouldn't he come home with glowing accounts of distant places, rich foreign fabrics and dark mysterious hints of high adventure in strange lands?

Nevertheless, as the river boat put in at the Manhattan docks, vague apprehensions shook his exultation somewhat, and for one brief moment he wondered if he should turn back. But it was too late. He was expected at the home of Alexander Bradford, his brother's friend, who had already begun to make arrangements for Herman to sail aboard the *St. Lawrence,* a merchant ship bound for Liverpool with a cargo of 100 bales of cotton.

For two days he stayed at the Bradfords', making preparations for the voyage while enjoying the kind hospitality of his brother's friend. First he went to the shipping office, to sign the ship's articles. He was number twelve on the crew list of sixteen men. Because of his scratchy signature, he was listed as "Norman" Melville

Aged	Height		Complexion	Hair
19	feet	inches	(light)	(brown)
	5	8½		

Beyond these few facts the ship's record demanded nothing except to ask his previous experience, and he had none to give. So the captain, Oliver P. Brown, a jovial man with a hearty laugh when signing up sailors, put young Melville down as a "boy," which meant that he could be assigned to any and all duties until he had served long enough and well enough to deserve the title of "seaman." (Many a ship's "boy" was a middle-aged or even an old man, going to sea for the first time.)

Once the signing was done, the "master" of the *St. Lawrence* turned cold and distant; he was not interested in helping the new recruit by advancing a month's salary for necessary supplies. Herman had to make out as best he could with the little money his mother and brothers had been able to spare. Leaving the office, he went to Catherine's Market near the wharves where he bought a red woolen sailor's shirt, the kind his cousin Tom—and most sailors—always wore; he bought a tarpaulin hat, a jackknife, and a few other items he thought might make his voyage comfortable.

On the last night he and Gansevoort had sat up late, talking, and his brother had given him an old hunting jacket, a little out-of-date, but heavy and warmly lined against the sharp ocean gales. The present came as something of a surprise from Gansevoort, the eldest of the eight Melville children, the one who had always been held up as brilliant, capable, in every way superior to Herman, the second son. ("Backward in speech and somewhat slow in comprehension," his father had described him when he was seven—although he added that the boy was "both solid and profound and of a docile and amiable disposition.")

Herman had not expected his older brother to take such an interest in his going to sea, and he accepted the jacket gratefully, though it was old-fashioned and rather clumsy, with far too many buttons. However, he decided to wear it instead of his own shabby coat.

The next morning he had boarded the *St. Lawrence,* still with a mixture of feelings inside him—shyness, uncertainty, wonderment, with the undercurrent of excitement and adventurousness running swiftly in his veins. The ship was a beehive of activity; a great many men were in the rigging, getting the *St. Lawrence* ready for sea. (They were "riggers," the young sailor found out later, men who lived ashore and only came on board to do their work just before sailing time.) Other men were bringing aboard the food supplies for the voyage—chickens, pigs, beef and vegetables. A man in a huge pea jacket—who turned out to be the second mate—was calling out orders to the riggers, and a man in a striped calico shirt under a short jacket was calling out orders to *him;* that was the first mate; and soon Captain Brown came up the side and "ordered about both of them," Herman commented to himself. The captain, who had seemed so friendly when Herman was signing the ship's articles, did not look in his direction but, if he had, he probably would not have taken any notice of the young new sailor nor shown any sign of recognition. Aboard ship, the captain was

king of his realm, spoke little except to issue orders, and those only to his first or second mate.

While the "greenhorn" Melville was standing there taking in the hustle and bustle, the chief mate turned away from the other two and ordered him to "clean out the pig pen in the long boat; it has not been cleaned since last voyage." He added, "And bear a hand about it, d'ye hear; there's them pigs there waiting to be put in; come, be off about it now."

At home Herman never would have thought of doing such a job, nor would he have been asked to do it; but he had been given an order and something in the chief mate's eye told him it would be dangerous to question the regularity of such an order. So he meekly asked for a spade or a shovel to work with, but the mate, with a surly grin, told him to "dig it out with his teeth!"

His first assignment was a sordid introduction to his life at sea. Looking around the deck, he found a stick and started scraping out the pen as best he could. When that was done, the mate came along again and ordered him to pick up the shavings the carpenters had left on deck that morning. He was to put them in a particular spot, between two of the seats in the long boat. It seemed easier to push them through a wider space, but when the mate caught him at it he roared, "Didn't I tell you to put those shavings somewhere else? Do what I tell you now or mind your eye!"

If he had asked "why?" the mate probably would have taken his head off. Sea officers, it appeared, never gave reasons for anything they ordered to be done. Enough that they commanded it. The motto of the ship, as Herman Melville, like all beginners, had to learn on his first voyage, was simply, "Obey orders, though you break owners." The mates were called "mister," and "sir" when orders were accepted. "Aye, aye, sir" was repeated so often it sounded almost like a single word.

In the little village school at home, he had been Mr. Melville, and his word, even though in a tiny domain, had been law. It was "Yes, Mr. Melville," "No, Mr. Melville," though he had been a mild sort of schoolmaster, young, dreamy eyed and more literary than scholarly. He found his pupils for the most part dull and thick witted, but they respected him, and if the school had not been forced to close he wouldn't have minded staying on longer.

Here, however, he was bullied and bossed about like the lowest menial, as the "boy" of any ship must expect to be. This was only the first day; they had not even left the docks at the foot of Jones Lane (Pier 14), where the *St. Lawrence* lay at anchor, and he had already received one command after another. As soon as he finished disposing of the shavings, the mate ordered him to "slush down the main-topmast," and although he knew what the main-topmast was, he had no idea what "slushing it down" meant. Some years later he wrote, "But the mate had turned on his heel, and made no explanations. At length I followed after him and asked what I must do."

"Didn't I tell you to slush down the main-topmast?" he shouted.

"You did," said I, "but I don't know what that means."

"Green as grass! A regular cabbage head!" he exclaimed to himself. "A fine time I'll have with such a greenhorn aboard. Look you, youngster. Look up to that long pole there—d'ye see it? That piece of a tree there, you timberhead—well—take this bucket here and go up the rigging—that rope-ladder there—do you understand—and dab this slush all over the mast, and look out for your head if one drop falls on deck. Be off now."

So he had to pick up the heavy bucket (at sea it was always a "bucket," never a "pail," he discovered) filled with grease and carry it to the top in the rigging. Once there, he had to start "dabbing the slush on the mast," as the mate had said, and keep on greasing as he worked his way down. It was no easy job, and from the top it was dizzying to look down, but he was determined to become a sailor and the only way to do it was to tackle any job that came up.

He breathed a sigh of relief, however, when he was safely back down on deck. Now the bustle had increased; the trunks of the few cabin passengers, the chests and boxes of steerage passengers and baskets of wine and fruit for the captain arrived. Last of all to come aboard were the crew who always stayed ashore till the final moment of sailing. When everything was ready, "the pilot

came on board, and all hands were called to up anchor."
Along with fifteen rough sailors, Herman Melville had
to man the huge windlass which hoisted the anchor. As
he worked his bar—and he had to push with all his
strength—he noticed that many of the seamen looked
haggard and weary after their shore leave and had to
strain harder than he. Yet none of them complained but
appeared "all alive and hearty," as they always did, no
matter how they felt, he learned.

When the anchor was secure, a tugboat took them in
tow, and the *St. Lawrence* started down to the sea—past
the long line of shipping, wharves and warehouses, past
the Battery and Governor's Island, pointing out for the
Narrows. Although he was busy, like the rest of the
crew, coiling cables and ropes, putting the decks in order,
the "boy" Melville stole farewell glimpses of his native
land as they went farther and farther down the bay. It
seemed incredible to him that he was actually sailing
away to a foreign shore, and when they passed Staten
Island, where he had so often gone with his father, he
suddenly wished the voyage were over, that they were
coming in to the bay instead of sailing out of it.

But the next time he looked up they had reached the
Narrows, "which everybody knows is the entrance to New
York harbor from the sea; and it may well be called
the Narrows, for when you go in or out, it seems like
going in or out of a doorway; and when you go out of
these Narrows on a long voyage . . . it seems like going
out into the broad highway, where not a soul is to be seen.
For far away and away stretches the great Atlantic
Ocean; and all you can see beyond it where the sky comes
down to the water."

By sunset they were "outside"; the breeze began to

blow, the sails were set, and shortly afterward the *St. Lawrence* cast loose from the tugboat and began to "roll" in the Atlantic, "as if it were a great barrel in the water." A little farther out a small schooner crossed her bows, and the pilot, issuing final orders of advice to Captain Brown, was transferred to it. The schooner passed under the stern, with her crew standing up waving their hats in cheering farewell. But nineteen-year-old Herman Melville, watching it disappear from sight, felt that it was the last of America he would see for a long time. He even wondered whether he would ever see his country again.

As soon as they were well "out," the entire crew was called to the quarter-deck to be divided into "watches." The two mates stood before the men and chose the ones they wanted to have under their command. The new boy was the last to be chosen, since he was green and untried, and neither mate was eager to take on a new hand. Herman's lot finally fell with the chief mate's, the larboard watch, and he was to "stand" with five other sailors the first night out. There were always six crew members for each watch on the *St. Lawrence,* and bells rang out every half hour; each watch lasted for eight bells.

This first-night duty was marked by moonlight and a soft breeze after the damp foggy weather, and most of the sailors sat on the windlass, exchanging stories of their leave, spinning out yarns of adventures that had taken place in cities that were only names to most people— Canton, Valparaiso, Bombay. They spoke them as familiarly as the Melville family mentioned New York or Albany or Pittsfield. Herman stood a little apart from the others, listening to the talk, somewhat disappointed to find that most of the sailors were interested only in the taverns and entertainment to be found in the various ports. He was certain that if he ever reached any of those places he would find a great deal more to do than visit taverns.

The first mate did not gossip with the men, but walked up and down the deck, smoking a long cigar, the lighted end like a torch in the darkness. Suddenly he stopped and gave an order to hoist one of the sails a little higher up on the mast. The sailors sprang to obey and Herman followed a step behind them because he wasn't sure what he should do. As soon as he saw them all take hold of the rope he grabbed it, too, and began to pull. In that moment a weird chant came from the man in the lead, a "song with no words to it, only a strange musical rise and fall of notes. In the dark night, and far out upon the lonely sea, it sounded wild. . . ." Herman almost looked around for goblins. He was so startled that he forgot to pull on the rope and the mate, who was standing near, pointed his cigar at him.

"Come, Boy, all hands alive!" he bellowed. "Can't you sing out at a rope?"

So he joined in the chant and somehow the song relieved the strain of pulling; it was a rhythmical way of getting the heavy job done and had a singular beauty of sound that was not quite music yet in a way was a great deal more—a magic ritual that made the men move as one.

However, although he had a resonant speaking voice, he had never been much of a singer, and the sailors poked fun at the noises that came out of his throat. "Did you hear the foghorn at the end of the line?" one of them jeered when they finished, and the others roared. They were rough, hard-spoken, hard-living men, with little or no education, and they had small consideration for an ex-schoolteacher learning the ropes on a merchant vessel as a common seaman. He stood apart from them again, this time not even bothering to listen to their chatter. The day had been intolerably long and he was tired.

When eight bells sounded at last he went below to the forecastle with the rest, where the ship's crew lived when they were not on duty. You had to grope your way down into the forecastle, which was black as night even in the daytime, the only light coming from the hole on deck which led to it; and the place "smelt so bad of old ropes and tar" that as Herman came down the hatch now he wished he could take his bedding on deck and sleep in the fresh salt air.

The forecastle was crowded with bunks, which looked like large wooden boxes, all around its sides, and the sailors' sea chests placed around wherever there was room between the bunks. Young Melville had put the large bundle containing his bedroll, and other things his mother had included to make him comfortable, on one of the bunks near the hatch (so he would get some ventilation occasionally at least) when he had come aboard that morning. Now he found his belongings had been moved to the bunk right at the head of the ship, squeezed between two others so close he could not put out his hand without touching them.

His bunk, or the one he had picked out, was occupied by an evil-looking old sailor, with sallow skin, a snaky eye and a cruel mouth, from the little the new sailor could make out in the murky light as the man stood up to go on deck for the next watch. When Melville somewhat fearfully asked why he had appropriated his bunk, the sailor flew into a terrible rage, saying that it had always been *his* bunk, because it was the best, and he was the best seaman. His word was law in the forecastle.

Fixing his evil eye on the bewildered boy, he threatened, "If you ever cross my path or get in my way again, I'll be the death o' you." He coughed, a harsh, rasping cough. "And if you ever stumble about in the rigging near me, I'll make nothing o' pitching you overboard." And with a hoarse cackle halfway between a cough and a guffaw, he lurched past a stunned Herman Melville up the hatchway. The other sailors said nothing. They were used to Jackson and his tyranny below deck and knew that every new boy had to get used to it, though occasionally some of the men stood up against it when he went too far. For a while they talked among themselves and then fell into a snoring sleep.

But there was no sleep for the young mariner. Aside from his unfortunate tangle with the wretched, evil dictator of the forecastle, he could hardly bear to stay in the airless hole, full of the mixed odors not only of tar and old rope now, but of tobacco juice, oilskins, stale sea biscuit and perspiring sailors, whose salt-sprayed clothes (in which they slept) became overheated in the narrow quarters. He sat on one of the chests, his face bent over his knees between his hands, and for a long time thought about the life he had left behind him—his life until that morning.

2

EARLY YEARS

HE HAD been born at No. 6 Pearl Street in New York City, on the first of August, 1819. At first there were only two other children to play with—his brother Gansevoort, the eldest child, and his sister Helen; but by the time he was two, there was a baby sister, Augusta. Then almost every year there was a new baby—Allan, Catherine, Frances-Priscilla and Thomas—until the household seemed overflowing with children, and the Melvilles kept moving to larger places in order to accommodate the growing family.

The house on Pearl Street was near his father's importing offices just off the Battery, but before Herman was two they had moved to 55 Cortlandt Street, near the landing of the Hudson River boat, on which they used to travel several times a year. For as long as he could remember—from the time he was only a month old, according to his mother—they had boarded the river boat every summer, and sometimes in winter or spring, to go north for a visit with his grandmother in Albany. This was his mother's mother who bore the old Dutch name of Gansevoort proudly, proud of her husband, who had been General Peter Gansevoort, famous defender of Fort Stanwix during the Revolution.

On the way back to New York, they would always stop in Boston to visit his father's parents. Grandfather Melville had taken part in the Boston Tea Party and loved to show the children the bottle containing the tea leaves he had brought home in the shoes of his Indian costume on that well-remembered night.

Sometimes, on the way back, the family from New York would stop in Pittsfield, Massachusetts, where Uncle Thomas Melville lived in a sprawling country home called "Broadhall," and tried to run the sprawling farm around it like a gentleman farmer, though he had very little money any more. He had gone to France, where he had made and lost a fortune in his early days, and some of the elegance still lingered about him. He would stop hoeing at the end of a row to pull out a dainty snuffbox and take a pinch of snuff.

Along with his brothers and sisters, Herman liked the visits to Broadhall best of all. Here the children could romp and race through the meadows to their heart's content, and their father didn't have to worry about their keeping out of the street the way he did in New York.

Between the Gansevoorts and the Melvilles, they made a large clan of aunts, uncles, cousins and grandparents, and there were always comings and goings of one sort or another.

From Cortlandt Street Mr. Melville moved his family uptown to Bleecker Street, to a pleasant house with a vacant lot next to it where the children could play. The boys, even little Allan, attended the "New York Male High School" five blocks away, which their father had helped establish. Here they were taught the usual subjects—as Herman wrote to his grandmother: "I now study Geography, Gramar, Arithmetic, Writing, Speaking, Spelling, and read in the Scientific Class book." But since there was only one teacher for every forty students, they used the monitor system: the teachers taught the best and quickest pupils; and those in turn led a little group of boys in reciting whatever they could learn by memory.

To the Melvilles' great surprise, Herman was made a monitor during his second year at the school, and what was more, won honors to rival Gansevoort's. His father wrote joyfully to Uncle Peter Gansevoort: "You will be as much surprised as myself to know that Herman proved the best speaker in the Introductory Department, at the examination of the High School; he has made rapid progress during the last 2 quarters."

As monitor, Herman gathered his group of eight boys into a corner of the large classroom every day and drilled them in "Arithmetic, the Tables, and Spelling." Then he would hear their set answers to the set questions in geography, and put down the number of correct and incorrect answers in his monitor's book. He never had much trouble with the boys he drilled because he never tried to lord it over them like some of the other monitors. Then, too, anyone who broke the rules of the school was tried by a boy jury and there were not many who wanted to be sentenced by their own classmates. So for the most part the pupils paid attention to the monitors, especially an "amiable" one like Herman Melville.

Twice a week the Melville children attended dancing school in a marble house on Broome Street. The boys always went into their mother's bedroom for her careful inspection before they left, while the governess fussed over the girls.

On Sundays, the whole family joined the procession which slowly marched to church three times a day—at ten o'clock, at three o'clock and at seven o'clock. The Knickerbocker sabbath was a day set apart strictly for worship, and nothing was allowed to interfere with the routine of prayer which started with the tolling of the bells in the quiet of Sunday morning. Herman remembered the endless hours of sitting between Gansevoort and Allan on one side of his parents in the Melville pew. Helen, Augusta and Catherine sat on the other, and Mrs. Melville held the baby, Priscilla, on her lap. It seemed to him that Reverend Brodhead would never finish preaching. And then what a relief it was to stand up for the benediction! It was long, too, but you could stretch your legs.

Then they walked back to Bleecker Street for a cold dinner, and back to church twice more before that cheerless day was over. Now a whole week lay ahead before the next ordeal—a week of playing in the vacant lot after school, of going to dancing school or occasionally to a party.

The next year the Melvilles moved to a new house at 675 Broadway, only two blocks from the old house but

in a much more fashionable neighborhood. Their new home, once the decorators had finished, was comfortable, spacious and elegant. Living here was the finest they had known or would ever know. Herman remembered the enormous family dinners at Thanksgiving when his mother provided "a famous turkey," "a large plum pudding," a barrel or two of cider, a variety of pies and all the other tempting foods that went to make up the feast of Dutch cookery.

There were many happy times in the house on Broadway. Even on rainy Saturdays, when they couldn't play outdoors, the children were never at a loss for something to do. If nothing else, Herman liked to look at the sea paintings and engravings which hung in the downstairs parlors and in the dining room. He liked to imagine how it would feel to be on the fat-looking, smoky fishing boat in one of the paintings which showed the men hauling in a seine. Or he tried to picture himself on one of the three French men-of-war, "with high castles, like pagodas, on the bow and stern," sailing on a bright blue sea.

Or, most exciting of all, he used to imagine himself part of the picture "of a great whale, as big as a ship, stuck full of harpoons, and three boats sailing after it as fast as they could fly." What a mighty thrill to be chasing an enormous whale across the wide ocean! He spent hours dreaming of different sea voyages when he should have been studying advanced arithmetic.

Occasionally Mr. Melville would let the boys visit him in his shop on Pine Street, not far from the New York waterfront when, before they went home, he would take them over to the crowded piers to watch the ships. Here were vessels from all over the world jostling each other, spilling cargoes and passengers from all over the world onto the wharves. As Herman stood with his father and brothers watching the busy scene, he resolved that some day he, too, would go abroad.

Life in New York's fashionable neighborhood went along pleasantly, with visits now and then from cousins going off to sea, like Guert Gansevoort, who was a midshipman on the *Constitution* and stayed at the Melvilles' before he shipped to the Mediterranean, and again three years later, when he returned from Africa. Herman listened eagerly to the stories of his travels, and to those of Guert's older brother, Peter, who had gone to sea as a common sailor and used to drop in at the Melvilles' when he was in port. And the more Herman Melville heard of their experiences, the more his fancy grew, until he imagined himself a sailor on the high seas.

What a difference between those beautiful dreams and the dark, dank forecastle of the *St. Lawrence!* Herman lifted his head for a moment and peered about him as the snoring of the men around him moved into his memories. If this was a sample of the lot of a sailor on the high seas, he might better have stayed home and gone on teaching or trying to write novels, the thing he really wanted to do, although he kept his ambition secret for the most part.

If his father had lived and business had prospered the way it did when they moved to Broadway, Herman might have become a writer when he was graduated from college; he might have led the life of a gentleman and, like his father, crossed the ocean many times as a cabin passenger instead of a common sailor.

But one day in the summer of 1830, Mr. Melville had come home from Pine Street nearly frantic with worry. One of his "creditors had refused an extension," he said. He looked defeated and tired, and although Mrs. Melville tried to cheer him, she looked worried, too. And shortly after that, the business had collapsed. Mrs. Melville, holding the new baby in her arms (this was Thomas, who had been born in January), called all the children together and told them they were going to move to Albany. Although she was happy at the thought of being near her relatives again, she hated to give up the house on Broadway, they all knew, and they felt the same way. It would be nice to be near Grandmother Gansevoort and Uncle Peter and all their cousins; but it would be hard to leave the home—the pleasant life—they loved in New York.

Mrs. Melville went up to Albany first with the girls and younger boys. Herman and Gansevoort stayed on in

New York for another month, "keeping Bachelor's Hall" with their father. It was a strange, mixed-up sort of life they led that month, with Mr. Melville trying to sell the remains of his business from his house, and creditors and appraisers coming and going all the time. Finally moving day arrived, and Mrs. Melville came down from Albany to oversee the event; she wanted to be sure that the little furniture the creditors had left them was not wrecked. She and Gansevoort left on the same boat with the furniture.

Mr. Melville and Herman were supposed to follow on the next boat, but a violent thunderstorm blew up while they were waiting at the Cortlandt Street dock. All that dreary October night they sat on the hard benches through the tedious hours till morning. At times Herman dozed off, leaning against his father's shoulder, but the fury of the storm outside did not let him sleep long, and to an eleven-year-old boy it seemed as if the night would never end. When morning finally came, and with it the calm, father and son boarded the boat wearily and stood at the rail as the *Swiftsure* moved up the Hudson River. It was the last time they would ever see New York together.

As Herman sat lost in his thoughts, the *St. Lawrence* rolled in the swell of the moonlit waves, and the sailors stirred in their sleep, unconsciously shifting position with the sway of the ship. An old salt in the bunk next to Herman threw out one leg in turning over, jamming it into the boy's ribs.

"Ow!" He jumped at the unexpected blow.

Two or three of the men woke up and growled, "Wot's going on?" "Pipe down!" and closed their eyes again;

and the man whose foot had struck him said, "Why 're ye sitting there, like a bump on a log, Boy? It's high time ye turned in!" Then he, too, dropped off into a heavy slumber once more.

Probably he should get some sleep, Herman supposed vaguely, but his bedroll was still untied on his bunk and he didn't feel like bothering with it. He hardly heard the sailors, anyway; he was too engrossed in remembering the past.

When the Melville family came to Albany, Grandmother Gansevoort and Uncle Peter, who lived in a big solid-looking double house—an old three-story Dutch mansion—on North Market Street, welcomed them with open arms. Uncle Peter kindly loaned them enough money to get started again and Grandmother Gansevoort, who looked very old and frail for the first time, helped them find a place to live. They rented a house only five doors away from hers, so the children could run back and forth as much as they pleased. Mr. Melville made new business connections with a company of furriers and was put in charge of the Albany office on South Market Street. It seemed as if everything would be all right after all.

Almost as soon as they came to town, Gansevoort and Herman were registered at the best school, the Albany Academy. Their father did not want them to miss the fall term because of the moving; so on October 15, five days after they were settled, Herman entered the "Fourth Department." Along with half a dozen boys his own age and three who were older, he studied geography, reading and spelling, penmanship, arithmetic, English grammar, natural history and Irving's catechisms of universal, Grecian, Roman and English history, classical biography and Jewish antiquities. Students were expected to study six hours a day, and the routine was rigid, the discipline very strict.

For the first time in their school lives, the Melville boys saw pupils being "birched," receiving so many strokes across the back with a stiff birch rod for the slightest misconduct. To Gansevoort and Herman the whole atmosphere of the school was stiff and strained, not to say cruel, after the New York school, where corporal punishment was almost unknown. Herman, especially, hated to see the birching, which raised great welts on the boys' backs; and which the principal, T. Romeyn Beck, a formidable-looking man with a crooked nose and a shock of hair like a frowsy wig, was likely to deal out at any hour. He was a good teacher, even gentle in his speech, but let any pupil be guilty of whispering or giggling during the principal's lectures and out came the rod; the boy had to bend over and receive his whacks. (Once fifty boys were birched for snowballing a farmer on their way home from school!)

The academy was stern in the matter of religion also. Prayers began and ended each day's study. The reading books included *Beauties of the Bible,* and Murray's *English Reader,* a volume of moral and religious writings, with one fourth of the contents devoted to sermons. Except for "ciphering," almost every subject was in some way related to religious thought and teaching. Herman sometimes felt as if he were going to church all week long. And often, when he walked up the steep hill toward the academy with Gansevoort and Allan, he longed to turn and run back down to their house or, better still, to Grandmother Gansevoort's.

The Melvilles' still seemed strange, but Grandmother Gansevoort's was just the same as it had always been, and it gave you a solid feeling to be in the roomy old house with its solid Dutch taste displayed in every room. There was an air of peace and security about the whole household, a quiet, well-padded homeyness that was like a balm after the confusion of the Melville household. Nearly every day saw Herman at his grandmother's and, whenever he could, he stayed all night.

But in December, only three months after the Melvilles had moved to Albany, Grandmother Gansevoort died suddenly, between Christmas and New Year's. The children could hardly believe their grandmother was gone, until they went to the funeral and tiptoed past the coffin with their Albany cousins. Nearly four hundred friends were present, too, outside of the family; statesmen, merchants, physicians, ministers and even booksellers came to the funeral of Catherine VanShaick Gansevoort. The town of Albany had lost one of its leading citizens, and Herman Melville, along with the rest of his family, had lost one of the leading, most stabilizing influences in his life.

The next year at school was easier; faces were familiar, the routine seemed natural and the work went more smoothly. And the next August, among the pupils who received prizes for excellence in various studies, Herman Melville marched up to the platform to accept his "premium." This was a book of famous writings, and in it the principal had inscribed the words:

"To Herman Melville
The first best in his class
in ciphering books.
T. Romeyn Beck, Principal."

Mr. Melville was especially proud of his son and wrote the news to all the relatives. Herman was glad, too, that he had finally won a prize after all the honors that Gansevoort had always received. Maybe now his older brother wouldn't be held quite such a genius. However, it was really not much of an accomplishment to win a prize in math and bookkeeping. How much better it would have been to be named "first best" in the classics or literature, or even oratory. One night, some time later, when everyone else had forgotten about his premium, Herman took his penknife and scratched out the words "in ciphering books." No need for those who might see the volume in the future to know the exact subjects in which he was "first best in his class"!

In the fall, Mr. Melville's business took a turn for the worse again. Although he worked very hard and went to New York to see what could be done to improve his sales, it was no use. Late in December, at just about the same time Grandmother Gansevoort had become ill the year before, Mr. Melville went to bed with a severe cold. He had had to cross the Hudson on foot a few nights before on his return from New York in freezing weather of two degrees below zero, and the exposure was too much for a tired, overworked man. He tried to keep going but Mrs. Melville finally insisted that he should take a few days' rest in bed.

But it was too late. Fever and chills set in and, although the doctors did everything possible to check it, his illness grew worse and worse. Uncle Peter wrote to Uncle Thomas, who came hurrying from Pittsfield. The whole family was tense with worry. The children spoke in whispers without being told. But nothing seemed to help, and on January 28, 1832, Mr. Melville died.

It was a hard blow for a twelve-and-a-half-year-old boy to bear, and Herman, like the rest of the Melville children, felt the loss keenly. Gansevoort took over his father's business, which was deeply in debt; Uncle Peter helped him pay off the debt and set up a new store selling caps, which were not as costly an investment as furs. Herman continued at the academy for a few months but in the spring he went to work in Uncle Peter's bank, serving as an apprentice clerk. He did not earn much money, but the little he brought home was a help, and his mother was spared the cost of his schooling.

After a year or so, working all day on a high stool at a bank desk, "ciphering" began to tell on him. His eyes burned from constant strain, he grew pale and thin from lack of fresh air and exercise; and he was very tired of recording bills and loans. He longed to get away from the humdrum routine of the bank. He thought more and more about the outdoor world as he sat indoors day after day; he thought of Broadhall and the farm at Pittsfield, of the fragrance of newmown hay and the round pond right in back of the house. And one day in the spring of 1834 he told his mother that he wanted to try living on the farm in Pittsfield for a while.

He arrived at Broadhall in early summer, and when his uncle met him "on the larch-shaded porch of the mansion looking off under urn-shaped roadside elms, across meadows to South Mountain," he remembered the times he had come there with his father and he felt a peacefulness steal over him that he had not known since those days.

Listening to Uncle Thomas that summer, even more than when he was a small boy, made Herman crave to go abroad, to see for himself the cities his father and uncle had traveled or lived in, to watch all the famous place names he had seen only in his imagination suddenly come to life before his eyes. That would be living!

And while he was at Broadhall, word came several times from his cousin Tom, who had sailed the South Seas aboard the U.S.S. *Vincennes*. Tom had been to distant points in the Pacific; romantic names like Tahiti, Hawaii, the Marquesas and the mysterious Typee Valley glowed from his letters like radiant jewels in his young cousin's eyes. Imagine crossing the Pacific, touching on strange lands, seeing strange people, tasting strange foods! To Herman, Cousin Tom's life seemed more alluring than any career at home could possibly be. And when they received word that Tom was shipping on a whaler in the spring, just before Herman went back to Albany, he was almost tempted to run away to sea himself, instead of going back to clerk in Gansevoort's cap store.

For his brother had written that he needed help in the store and, since Herman had been away almost a year, it was high time he returned to take part in the family business. The Melvilles had moved to a better house, at No. 3 Clinton Square; and Uncle Peter, who had recently married, had moved to No. 1, just two doors away. They all wanted Herman to share the new house, to be in his own family circle again. At Broadhall he had put on some weight besides growing husky and tan; he was in much better condition than when he came. But if he was needed at home he had to go.

The new house in Albany was comfortable, even elegant, and the girls (Helen, Augusta and Catherine) were attending the Albany Female Academy—Gansevoort was doing very well with the store. Herman became his assistant and for the next two years worked with him as a bookkeeper and clerk, selling "brush hats of the finest quality" in the summer, and fur caps, buffalo or racoon sleigh robes when the winter set in. Gansevoort paid him five dollars a week, enough to give him the independence he needed for his interests outside the business.

He began to read enormously, borrowing books from the Albany library, of which Uncle Peter was a member. Before Herman went to Broadhall, he had found some first-rate novels in his uncle's private library, especially one called *The Red Rover* by James Fenimore Cooper. (Uncle Peter was a friend of Cooper, who had autographed the book.) What a fascinating story that was! It was the first time he had come across a book that stirred his imagination so completely—that made him lose himself in the unfolding of a tale, without getting bored by moral lessons. Here was a historical picture of America set down in an interesting and dramatic style, so that you felt you were actually living through those early exciting times. Now he read more of Cooper and went on to Byron and the romantic novels of Sir Walter Scott, lapping them up with a voracious appetite.

He entered the Albany Classical School, which had just opened across the square from the Melvilles', attending classes after the day's work was over. He took great interest in writing themes, because they gave him a chance to express some of the ideas that came to him through his reading and through long hours of pondering about life while he was tilling the earth at Uncle Thomas'.

He and Gansevoort both joined the Albany Young Men's Association, a literary club which had a debate hall and comfortable reading rooms not far from the store. Here members could read the latest newspapers and magazines or browse in the library if they did not care for the political discussions which took place whenever a little knot of members gathered. In the library Herman discovered the works of Thomas Moore and the *Arabian Nights,* which sent his imagination soaring, and he took his own flights of fancy in short sketches, stories of poetic fantasy written out of boyish enthusiasm. Here he also read Shakespeare, Coleridge and Chesterfield; and he had his first taste of philosophy in the writings of Locke and Newton.

He attended the lectures given at the association and the debates in which Gansevoort took part. The debating group died down after a few months, however, and Herman joined the Philo Logos Society, a group of lawyers, teachers, businessmen and painters, who took an active interest in art, letters and public affairs.

He might have gone on that way for the rest of his days, except that a financial depression fell on the country in 1837 and Gansevoort, like thousands of other small businessmen, was practically wiped out. He was not well and could not even try to gain back his losses. He declared bankruptcy in April and a few weeks later Mrs. Melville did the same.

The family was forced to live off the little Uncle Peter could spare, since he had gone into debt himself during the depression. Poor Gansevoort became really ill and had to go to bed. Allan and the girls had to interrupt their education; and Herman, who could find nothing to do in Albany, took a job teaching school near Pittsfield.

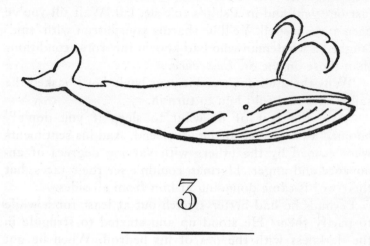

3

"SCHOOLTEACHER" MELVILLE

A SUDDEN SCRATCHING noise in the side of the ship broke
into the young mariner's reverie, and a moment later he
started up with a shudder as a huge black rat ran across
his feet. A big, long-tailed rat! Moving instinctively to
get away from the spot, Herman's foot struck the next
chest with a loud bang and he stumbled, falling headlong
over it!

This time the sailors all woke up. They groaned and
cursed.

"Now wot?"—"The greenhorn agin, blast 'im!"
"Whadda ye think ye 're trying to do, boy?"

"There's a rat in here."

His answer brought jeers and hoots of derision from his shipmates. "Now, ain't that too bad!" "It won't be the last one ye'll find in a ship's fo'c'sle, lad. Wait till you've been at sea a spell. Ye'll be sharing your biscuit with 'em," laughed a whaleman who had known far worse conditions than those on the *St. Lawrence*.

"Why the divil don't ye hit your bunk, boy?" asked the sailor who had told him to turn in.

"Aye, the rest of us want to sleep if you don't!" boomed a bass voice at the other end. And his sentiments were echoed by the others with varying degrees of annoyance and anger. Herman couldn't see their faces, but their words came pounding at him from all sides.

Perhaps he had better stretch out at least for a while to pacify them. He stood up and started to struggle in the darkness with the ties of his bedroll. When he got them undone, he opened the roll and lay down without bothering to smooth out the blankets or climb under them. The bunk was like a bare plank, even with the bedding. He thought of the great mahogany bedsteads at Grandmother Gansevoort's old house, where you slept on double mattresses with down feather-beds to cover you, and his sailor's bunk seemed to grow harder and harder. Lying down like this the air was even more stifling, and the constant roll of the ship more noticeable. He didn't understand how the sailors could sleep the way they did, unconscious of it all.

Tired as he was, he found himself unable to relax. He could hear the rat gnawing at the wood, trying to break through to a small pantry under the hatchway. It made him nervous and uneasy; he was used to the field mice that scampered into the house when he was on the farm, but they were one thing—a rat was quite another. After a while he couldn't bear to lie down any longer. He sat up, resting his head between his hands again.

Maybe he should have stayed at home and tried a little harder to get another teaching job. He had become used to the work which was dull, but not impossible. He smiled when he thought of his first few weeks as a schoolteacher. Uncle Thomas had helped him secure the job, which was at the Sykes District School, a little one-room building at the fork of the roads leading to New Lenox and Washington County. Poor Uncle Thomas had gone west to Galena, Illinois, to seek a new fortune, leaving his oldest son Robert to run Broadhall; but before he left he had headed a committee investigating schools. He found them much in need of teachers and recommended his nephew for the post at Sykes.

When Herman came into the small, weather-beaten building the first morning, it looked barren and bleak. Bare wooden benches took up most of the space, and on a raised platform at one end stood a wobbly wooden table—his desk, no doubt, he thought wryly. Behind it was a smeary blackboard, and in the corner huddled a small iron coalstove, its door half open on a rusty hinge. That was all.

He stepped on the platform and flung his books on the table. A cloud of dust rose on all sides. He took out his handkerchief and batted the film off lightly. He would give the table a proper cleaning the next day. The benches would have to be dusted by the backs of the pupils. He went outside and pulled the rope of the schoolhouse bell in its tower of flaking clapboard. As it ding-donged a wheezy warning over the countryside he noticed several figures far down the road break into a sprint, heading for the school like charging bulls. He went back inside in order to be busy when the classroom started filling up.

Pushed under the table was the bottom half of a rickety chair that he had not even noticed before. He pulled it out, blew off the dust and sat down, opening his books; here was one Uncle Peter had given him before he left Albany: *The District School,* by John O. Taylor, which described all the trials and tribulations of teaching in a school like this. From the shouts that were now almost outside the door, Herman had a premonition that he was going to experience a few of those trials himself.

At last the door opened, and three little girls walked in; when he nodded to them, they giggled shyly and took three seats on the front bench. Next a group of boys and girls burst in, laughing and teasing each other. The room filled up rapidly after that; the back bench was occupied by the biggest boys, who stayed outside wrestling and shouting until the final moment when the new teacher came out to ring the tardy bell. Then they all hustled in, eying him curiously.

Several of them were nearly full-grown men his own age, eighteen, and they were measuring his strength with theirs. What they saw was a mild-appearing, round-faced young man with a cleft in his chin, rather small blue eyes and overlarge ears—a little broad in the shoulders, but no bigger than they were certainly. One of them winked knowingly at the others. They could handle Mr. Herman Melville, the new teacher!

As for the "new teacher" himself—he sat looking over his "scholars" with a somewhat sinking heart. Thirty of them in front of him, of all ages, sizes, ranks, characters; he would soon find out about their education so far. He rapped for order, but aside from the two front rows, nobody paid the slightest attention. He stood up. He said in a loud authoritative voice: "We will all recite the Lord's prayer."

That much they all knew. Arithmetic seemed to be unknown territory, even to those who had gone through it before. Two of the eighteen-year-olds didn't know that two and two made four. Geography was not much better. He tried asking the first question of one of the five children belonging to the farmer he was boarding with—a real "Yankee character" who lived on top of a lonely mountain a mile and a half from the school. However, all five of them shook their heads and grinned silently. Of history, even American history dealing with the pilgrims and Indians who had lived and fought in the neighborhood, these "students" had only the vaguest idea.

Every now and then there were interruptions, when one or the other of the littlest ones had to be led to the outhouse by an older brother or sister. Around the middle of the morning a spit-ball battle started in the back row among the oldest boys. At first he paid no attention to it, but when one of them boldly sent a pellet flying to the front of the room, right in the middle of the table, he got up and announced: "The next pupil who throws a spit-ball will remain after school for one hour." He nodded to the girl who had been reading. "Continue, Abigail."

A few minutes later, another pellet landed ping! on his table, while a titter of laughter ran over the room. He glanced up and said mildly but firmly: "The three gentlemen in the back of the room will remain after school to scrub the floors and wash the windows." It had occurred to him that he might as well get the building cleaned up at the same time he was meting out penalties.

But his half-wild charges hooted and muttered at his words. "Who says so?" "Try and make us!" One of them bawled out, "How do you know we threw 'em anyway?" And another one growled, "We gotta work in the fields after school."

"You should have thought of that sooner," Herman said. He repeated the penalties.

Somehow the day passed, with a break in the middle, when they all opened their lunch boxes and munched the homemade bread along with whatever could be spared from frugal New England larders.

When classes were finally over, the three older boys sullenly stayed behind. There were a couple of old tin pails and a mop in the outhouse, and with these he set them to work. When they finished, he locked the schoolhouse and tramped up the mountainside to the home of the Yankee farmer. His landlord was a "shrewd, bold and independent man," he wrote to Uncle Peter, perfectly free in handing out his opinions, and inclined to be gossipy. He informed Herman that the three who had been so troublesome in school had been thrashed by their fathers for being late because they had to stay after school.

"And so they should've been, the young scoundrels!" he added.

"But I didn't mean to get them into such trouble at home," Herman said earnestly.

"Won't hurt 'em none. Their skin's thick enough," the farmer said drily. "Mebbe after this they'll settle down some."

But the boys, although they were not quite so open in their pranks, still continued to disrupt the classes by one

CO. SCHOOLS

means or another; and they vowed they would get even with the teacher. They would pay him back, all right! And one night the following week, when Herman went to the general store for notebooks and chalk and erasers, he noticed the boys lounging outside. He smiled at them, but they looked away, and when he came out, they were not there. He started home.

It was early evening, just turning into darkness as he reached the outskirts of the village. He started up the lonely mountain road and had walked about half a mile when he heard a rustling in the bushes at the side, and a moment later three figures rushed at him, jumping on him from the back. Two of them tried to pin his arms down, while the third landed a blow on his chin.

But he was too quick for them. Surprised as he was, he wrenched himself free with one swift movement and managed to dodge his head so that the blow only glanced his chin. His own fists shot out like lightning once he was clear, first landing on one of his assailants and then another. The third, who attempted to grab him, he wrestled with and threw headlong on the ground. Then he exchanged blows with the other two again, but so sure was his aim that he was able to land two for every one of theirs, and when he knocked one of them to the ground so hard he couldn't get up, the other two cried out, "You win, Mr. Melville!"

The struggle had all taken place in a few minutes and in complete silence; Herman had not had time to recognize his pupils and he stared at them in astonishment through the darkness. The boys from school were actually trying to beat him up! How savage civilization still was, and how much they must have wanted to get even with him! He calmly straightened his clothes and picked up his packages.

"I hope you will be on time for school tomorrow morning, gentlemen," he said quietly, and continued climbing up the mountain.

After that, he had very little trouble as far as discipline went in the country school. The three bullies were not only subdued, but were filled with admiration for a teacher who could handle all of them at once and get the better of them. Word spread around that "Mr. Melville" was a great deal stronger than he looked, a first-rate boxer and not a man to be trifled with. By December, he could write to Uncle Peter that he had "brought his school under a proper organization," and he took some satisfaction in the fact that things were run quite smoothly in his little building, considering all the inconveniences.

But life in a country village community was dull, and

there were many times when he wished to be back in Albany. He began to wonder whether the Philo Logos Society had died out or if someone else was running it. He missed the Albany library and the occasional shows that came to town. In Sykes he could find nothing to do outside of school except attend church every Sunday and read what books the meager library had to offer. There were few people he could talk to outside of the farmer's family he lived with and there was no one he could converse with.

However, he stuck to the job for the whole term, and then the county board announced that funds had run out; the education of farmers' children would have to be discontinued. He was discouraged, but in a way he was relieved. He was too restless to be satisfied with the career of a country schoolteacher.

As the motion of the sea rolled the *St. Lawrence* through the darkness of the night he wondered what it was that made him unable to settle down to some little job like so many of the boys who had gone to the academy. In spite of the depression, most of them seemed to find something to do and were not too dissatisfied with their lot. Back in Albany after the Sykes school closed, he had nothing to do, so he busied himself by starting up the Philo Logos Society again. He called a meeting and had himself elected president, even though he had heard that someone else had been serving in the meantime, a young man named Van Loon. When the *Albany Microscope* published the names of the newly elected officers, Van Loon publicly denounced the whole reorganization and attacked Herman Melville in particular.

Herman replied with a fiery, scholarly and bitter letter,

which was also published. He denounced the other president as a "silly and brainless *loon,*" who stood "in the
van" of that "class of individuals who are of so narrow-
minded and jealous a disposition. . . ." and was more
than pleased with his pun on his rival's name. The exchange of public letters, written in high-sounding, strong
language, went on for nearly two months. Neither of the
"authors" had ever seen himself in print before, and they
both made the most of it.

But the whole literary swordplay was merely a means
of diversion against the dismal, growing poverty at home
which Herman was unable to relieve. It was then that
Mrs. Melville decided to move to Lansingburgh, a small
village twenty miles up the Hudson from Albany, where
living would be much cheaper. She found a modest but
pleasant house right on the river, and they settled down
to a quiet village life.

Herman was still without a job and the country was
still too deep in the depression to permit county schools
to reopen. Uncle Peter suggested that he take a course in
surveying and engineering at the Lansingburgh Academy.
The news had just been announced that the Erie Canal
was going to be expanded and there would probably be
several openings for young engineers. So back to school
he went, this time as a pupil, and glad of it.

But when the course was completed no post was open
for a green graduate, so he occupied his time writing
literary pieces for the pleasure of putting words together,
telling a story or posing some question in an essay. One
day he decided to submit the little article he had done in
the form of letters to the only newspaper in town, the
Democratic Press and Lansingburgh Advertiser. It was a

daring step. He did not want to sign his name for fear his writing might be rejected and his family, especially Gansevoort, would think him an utter fool. He put down instead the initials, L.A.V.

Every evening he scanned the columns eagerly for his work or some mention of it; the letters in the *Albany Microscope* had given him a taste for seeing his words in print, and he was hungry for more. Nearly a week went by and then a little notice appeared on a back page: "The communication of 'L.A.V.' has been received," it read. "An interview with the writer is requested."

L.A.V. They meant his "communication"! He borrowed Gansevoort's best coat, shined his shoes with stoveblack, slicked down his heavy brown hair and rushed to the editor's office. A seedy-looking man with an eyeshade over his forehead interviewed him for not more than half an hour when he suggested that Herman write a regular column for the paper which would be printed once a week as a voluntary contribution. Herman agreed at once. He had heard the editor stress the word "voluntary," but he didn't care. He didn't expect to be paid anyway. What did that matter? He was going to be published like an accepted author and the editor had praised his style.

He walked home along the river with a singing heart. Gansevoort wasn't the only one in the family with brains! He, Herman Melville, had a mind of his own and a great deal he was longing to express. He felt a little firmer, more sure of himself as he strode along the river bank.

As soon as he reached the house, he went up to his room, took out paper and pencil and sat down to write. He thought of all kinds of fancy titles for his column, using classical names in Latin or Greek; but none of these, he decided, was suitable for a village paper. He finally hit upon "Fragments from a Writing Desk," and let it go at that.

The first contribution he had sent in was published on the fourth of May, and the first "Fragment" appeared on the eighteenth. It was a small satire on the mystery romances of the time. He pictured himself a handsome gentleman in a "heavy cloak" who was handed a note by a strange, mysterious woman as he was resting on the "turf" by the river. He read the note, which summoned him to come to the chamber of an unknown love who admired him very much. The mysterious messenger beckoned him to follow her to a noble palace and there led him before a beautiful but silent woman. Not a word would she speak in answer to any of his entreaties, and he suddenly realized that she was deaf and dumb. *Deaf and dumb!* What an end to his wonderful dream of romance!

Herman's sisters thought the story very clever and humorous; they had not suspected their second brother could be so witty. Gansevoort admitted that his younger brother had a gift for storytelling, though he wasn't sure he approved of such literary clowning. Mrs. Melville was pleased to see her son's work in print but she was too taken up with worry over her debts to give the matter much thought.

"You really ought to find some work to do; I don't know how I can manage much longer on what Uncle Peter sends us," she fretted.

"Poor Mother!" Herman felt sorry for her, always trying to keep up appearances, retaining a "hired girl" they couldn't pay so that nobody would know how badly off they were. "I'll start out tomorrow and tramp around

here to see if any of the farmers can use my services. Or
there may be some school I've overlooked. Don't worry!"

He set off on foot the next morning and spent several
days going from one village to another, but neither the
farmers nor the school boards needed his services; he
returned home, discouraged and disgusted. The first thing
his mother told him was that Gansevoort had felt a little
stronger and decided to go to New York to visit Alexander Bradford. Perhaps his friend could find him a place
in a law office. Allan, too, was going to New York for
work.

That evening Herman sat on the front piazza, watching the river boats that plied slowly up and down the Hudson, some of them only sloops with lowly deck-loads of
hay and lumber. As he sat there, gazing dreamily at them
while he pondered on what he should try now, they suddenly changed into great masted sailing vessels with
cargoes of silks and satins, bound for distant lands.

An idea had come to him: he would go to sea! He got
up abruptly and went indoors to write a letter to Gansevoort; perhaps his brother and Bradford between them
could get him a place before the mast in one of the many
ships sailing soon for foreign shores.

Within a few days Gansevoort answered his letter.
They had made arrangements for Herman to become a
sailor, on the *St. Lawrence,* leaving the last week in May
or shortly thereafter. And so he had gone to sea. . . .

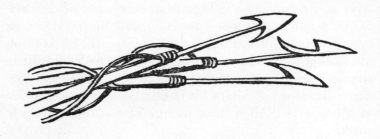

4

LIFE ABOARD THE ST. LAWRENCE

HERMAN AWOKE with a start. A loud thumping on the deck above him had pulled him out of the uneasy slumber into which he had fallen, still with his head in his hands. His body felt cramped and achy. He had been dreaming of home and his mother's troubles in paying the grocer and the landlord; now he woke up to new ones of his own—the strange, dark forecastle, the sailors with their grizzly, unshaven faces, the sudden memory of the night before when that evil-eyed Jackson had threatened him for nothing at all. He shivered.

"Come, Boy!" One of his new shipmates clapped him

on the shoulder. "Can't ye hear that handspike the mate is pounding? It's our watch again already. Up, my hearty, up!"

And although he felt anything but hearty, Herman had to drag himself up on deck after no more than half an hour's doze during the whole night. Indeed, it had been only a few hours since they had come down—the ship's bells were ringing the hour of four in the morning. The first signs of dawn were just beginning to appear when they came up on deck. Luckily, all the sailors were still feeling groggy from their days of leave and they sat around on the windlass, or whatever else there was available, nodding and dozing till it got light. Herman was glad they were so silent and sleepy; it gave him a chance to catch a few more winks and he preferred snoozing on deck in the fresh salt air, even though he was standing up, to the miserable bunks in the airless hole of the forecastle.

But all too soon the sun began to shine, and the mate gave an order to "wash down the decks." The sailors stirred themselves, yawning and stretching, and got to work. Not knowing exactly what to do, Herman watched them a moment or two before plunging in himself. Since nobody was going to give him any instruction evidently, he could only learn by observation. If he could help it, he wasn't going to ask any unnecessary questions and make a laughingstock of himself. Most of the men were contemptuous of him as it was, because he was a "greenhorn."

Now they pulled a great tub into the waist, or middle, of the ship, and filled it with sea water drawn up in a bucket suspended on a long rope. The bucket was lowered and lifted many times before the tub was full enough to suit the second mate but he finally bellowed, "All right, grab your brooms and start scrubbin'!" Then the men took off their boots and began to scrub the decks hard with the stiff, short-handled brooms that were kept in one of the lifeboats for that purpose. They sloshed around in the water without seeming to mind, although even on a spring morning like this it felt cold; Herman wondered what it would be like on a winter morning in an icy gale. Scrubbing seemed more like housemaids' than sailors' work, but the men were used to it as part of the day's routine.

At eight o'clock the bell was struck again and they all went to breakfast. First every sailor went to the cook-house with his tin pot or cup or whatever he had brought and got it filled with coffee; then they went down into the forecastle to eat. A small tub, or "kid," the sailors called it, filled with a kind of cornmeal mush which they called "burgoo," was handed down the hatchway, containing enough for everybody. But instead of being dished out, the kid of burgoo was a sort of community pot, into which each man had a turn to dip his spoon. And what was worse the bowl was presided over by the horrible sailor known as Jackson. As soon as the kid appeared, he grabbed it in his scrawny hands, put it between his knees and began to pour into it some black molasses that had been handed down with the kid. He scooped out a little hole in the middle and poured in the sweet sticky stuff, so that it looked "for all the world like a little black pool in the Dismal Swamp of Virginia."

The sailors all stood around watching him, and now Herman was able to get a good look at the one who had threatened him the night before. He was like a man who had just recovered from yellow fever—Herman thought

—"as yellow as gamboge, and no more whisker on his cheek than I have on my elbows." Jackson's "hair had fallen out, and left him very bald, except in the nape of his neck and just behind the ears, where it was stuck over with short little tufts and looked like a worn-out shoe-brush. His nose had broken down in the middle, and he squinted with one eye, and did not look very straight out of the other. He was dressed a good deal like a Bowery boy . . . wearing a pair of great over-all blue trousers, fastened with suspenders, and three red woolen shirts, one over the other . . . and he had a large white wool hat, with a broad, rolling brim."

Watching Jackson pour the molasses like a sorcerer mixing a deadly potion, Herman decided he was nothing but the "foul lees and dregs of a man; he was as thin as a shadow, nothing but skin and bones." It was strange that the sailors bowed to the will of such a miserable piece of a man, but they did. They were formed in a circle around him now, waiting patiently until he cackled: "One at a time, now!" and then they dipped their spoons into the mush, one after another. When Herman started to stick his spoon in, Jackson rapped him on the knuckles with his spoon. "What d'ye think ye're doin', Boy?"

"Trying to get some burgoo," Herman answered, trying not to look at the ugly face.

"Burgoo ain't fer boys, it's fer tars!" cackled the evil-eyed sailor; and although it wasn't much of a joke, the rest of the men roared with laughter, shouting and clapping each other on the shoulder.

While the "boy" was turning from one to another in bewilderment, an old seaman, a Greenlander by birth—the same man who had spurred him into getting on deck that morning, slipped around in back of the circle and nudged him. "Psst . . . Boy, you're supposed to be on the other side, with the larboard watch."

So that was it. Herman was glad he had one friend, at least. But by the time he got around to his side, there was not much left there and he had to be content with two mouthfuls. Not that he wanted much more; the burgoo was a far cry from the home-cooked cereal he was used to—and when he remembered the silver porringers at Grandmother Gansevoort's or even the Dutch china in his mother's home, he wondered if he could stand to dig into the "kid" every morning.

After the burgoo was gone, they all sat around in a circle, cross-legged on their chests, eating salt beef and biscuit and drinking the coffee from their tin pots. The coffee was more like boiled cheese rinds or potato peelings, unlike any brew he had ever tasted. And the biscuit was rock-hard, so that the sailors broke it "very sociably" over each other's heads, which was quite convenient, but made his head ache for two or three days until he got used to it.

As the sailors ate, they told stories of their adventures, mostly gory tales of things that happened on this voyage or that, hardly what you would call appetizing. And the goriest of all came from Jackson—how the men died of fever when his ship was lying in Batavia, how he found a hooded cobra under his pillow in India, how sailors were poisoned in Canton and how ships were plundered by Malay ruffians in the straits of Gaspar. His whole talk was full of "piracies, plagues and poisonings. He seemed to be full of hatred and gall against every thing and every body in the world; as if all the world was one person, and had done him some dreadful harm, that was rankling and festering in his heart."

Herman sat quietly listening to all this talk. He thought it would probably be wisest to be quiet most of the time, at least until he knew the ropes. He had not escaped Jackson's evil eye, and the man was evidently dead set on being an enemy; but still he could keep out of the tyrant's way as much as possible, and this he meant to do.

The second day at sea the weather turned suddenly warm, a bright blue day, sky and water all deep blue, with the sun shining down on the decks so that they seemed warm and inviting instead of "dim and lonely." The men threw off their jackets. Gansevoort's old hunting jacket certainly was too much for a day like this; Herman threw it on his bunk in the forecastle and left it there.

If only there had been no work to do, if he could have lounged against the bulwarks, watching the little fleeces of foam on the ocean and listening to the strange musical noise the ship was making under her bows as she glided along. Or if they would have let him go out on the bowsprit and lie down between the manropes and look over at the fish in the water—oh, then how he could have enjoyed his first voyage!

But there was work to be done and though he felt as if he were in a dream, moving with the wonderful rising and falling of the blue sea, he had to help the men get the stunsails ready to hoist aloft. These sails were of light canvas and were hoisted way out beyond the ends of the yards when the wind was fair, "where they overhung the wide water, like the wings of a great bird."

The sailors started fastening them to the booms and the mate called out to Herman to tie one of the lines or ropes, but as each had a special name he had to ask which it was.

"Greenhorn, timberhead!" roared the mate. He pounded his forehead with his fist. "Oh, why do I always get the new boys?"

The sailors laughed and winked to each other, glad of a little diversion in the course of duty. After that Herman tried not to ask any questions but waited to see what the men did, or spoke in a whisper to the Greenlander, who pointed out what was to be done without uttering a word, so the others wouldn't know. It was good to have one ally, at least.

The task was finally finished, and with a completely new kind of thrill young mariner Melville saw the sails be spread. Many years later, he wrote of this moment: "At last we hoisted the stunsails up to the topsail yards, and as soon as the vessel felt them, she gave a sort of a bound like a horse, and the breeze blowing more and more, she went plunging along, shaking off the foam from her bows, like foam from a bridle-bit. Every mast and timber seemed to have a pulse in it that was beating with life and joy; and I felt a wild exulting in my own heart, and felt as if I would be glad to bound along so round the world.

"Then was I first conscious of a wonderful thing in me, that responded to all the wild commotion of the outer world; and went reeling on and on with the All. A wild bubbling and bursting was at my heart, as if a hidden spring had just gushed out there; and my blood went tingling along my frame, like mountain brooks in spring freshets."

That was the way he was feeling on the first fair morning of his first voyage, when the *St. Lawrence* suddenly started to "bound" over the Atlantic. It was as if he had suddenly been released from all the petty troubles and worries of home, from Gansevoort's older-brother rule, from his mother's gentle nagging, from all the rest of it, and now he was merging with the whole wide world of space—the limitless blue of ocean and sky, and the blue beyond that, so infinite you could hardly breathe when you thought of it. He stood with rapt eyes, gazing up at the stunsails billowing out in the breeze, a country boy in tight pants with the drumbeat of poetry pounding somewhere deep inside him.

"Boy! Melville!" came the harsh voice of the second mate from a great distance away. "Go clean out the chicken coop and make up the beds of the pigs in the longboat. What 're ye doing? Star-gazing in the morning? Hurry along now!"

It was a rough awakening from a beautiful dream. He had felt dreamy the whole morning until this moment and he had almost fallen in love with the life of the sea. Now as he went toward the chicken coop, he felt like the lowest menial, like a slave constantly ordered around. He wished with all his heart the voyage was over!

And the worst of it, he thought morosely as he cleaned out the chicken coop and the pigsty, was that none of the sailors ever got a bite of chicken or pork. No, indeed— that was for the captain, and the few passengers aboard ship. The poor people in the steerage had to furnish their own food supplies, and the sailors got nothing but salt beef and biscuit at every meal—and of course the inevitable burgoo at breakfast.

Still, the fresh ocean air gave him a sharp appetite and he found himself putting away as much salt beef and biscuit at dinner as any of the old "tars," and he learned to crack his biscuit over the heads of his neighbors and not to wince when he felt the bang on his own head. But never once did he try to break his biscuit over Jackson's head!

Nor did any of the others. Jackson was lord of the forecastle and no one dared dispute his rule.

The next night out of port the young mariner had his first taste of "going aloft" at sea. It was during the middle watch; the sea was calm and the breeze was mild. Herman stood hanging over the bow of the ship, watching the magic phosphorescent lights of the ocean as they shot out of the darkness. They were part of the wonder of the sea he was discovering, part of the mysterious power and beauty of it that he had dreamed about way back on Bleecker Street. When he stood like this, staring down fascinated by the fiery glow that came up out of the depths, he forgot the evils of the forecastle, the coarseness of the men and the smelly job of cleaning out the longboat.

"Loose the main-skysail!" came an order from the chief mate, almost like a call from another world.

"That's 'boy's business'!" was the next thing he heard, but he still didn't pay much attention until he heard his own name bawled out in no uncertain tones. "Boy—Melville!"

He turned away from the fireworks in the water.

An old Dutchman named Max came up to him. "It's boy's business to loose de royals," he said, "and not old men's business, like me."

"That's right," joined in one or two of the others, and a third added, "It's high time you were stirring yourself, and doing real boy's business!"

"Which one is it?" Herman asked Max quietly.

"D'ye see dat leetle fellow way up dare?" Max pointed a gnarled sailor's finger at the sky. *"Dare,* just behind dem stars dare: well, tumble up and looze him."

Without asking any more questions, Herman jumped

into the rigging. Up, up, up he went, "not daring to look down," but keeping his eyes glued to the shrouds. It was a long way up those ratlines; he began to pant and breathe hard before he was halfway there, but he kept on and on, till he got to the Jacob's Ladder, which was well named, for it took him almost into the clouds. He climbed that and at last, to his own amazement, found himself hanging on to the skysail yard! He held onto the mast with might and main and curled his feet around the rigging, "as if they were another pair of hands."

For a few moments he could do nothing but stand there, struck with wonder. He couldn't see far out on the ocean, it was so dark, but from that lofty perch, "the sea looked like a great, black gulf, hemmed in all round, by beetling black cliffs." It was as if he were all alone, treading the midnight clouds; at any second he expected to find himself falling—falling—falling, as in a sort of nightmare. He could just make out the ship below, like a narrow plank in the water; it didn't seem to belong at all to the yard over which he was hanging. A sea gull, flying around the truck over his head, almost frightened him with the whispering sound of its wings close to his face; "it seemed so much like a spirit, at such a lofty and solitary height."

He was lost in the world on high and nearly forgot what he was about; but presently he heard a distant, hoarse noise from below. He knew it must be the mate hurrying him. Nervous and trembling, he started casting off the gaskets or lines tying up the sail. He worked in a kind of frenzy, and when it was all ready, he sang out, as he had been told, "Hoist away!"

And hoist they did, so quickly that he went up right along with the yard and sail! It was like magic—there he was going higher and higher, the yard rising under him, "as if it were alive, and no soul in sight." Something told him he was in danger; he held on hard, and when the sail was in place he climbed down the rigging as fast as he could go. Once on deck, Max clapped him on the shoulder and said that for a new boy he had done very well.

Max was a bachelor, who "prided himself greatly on his seamanship, and entertained some strait-laced, old-fashioned notions about the duties of boys at sea. His hair, whiskers, and cheeks were of a fiery red, and as he wore a red shirt, he was altogether the most combustible looking man" Herman Melville had ever seen. He had a very inflammable temper and more than once had been known to let it fly against Jackson's tyranny. He resented the rule of the evil sailor and was ready to instigate a rebellion at any time. He tried to influence the new "boys" to stand up with him and overthrow the dictator of the forecastle.

He was fond of giving advice, and after Herman had proved that he could learn to be a sailor by the way he handled the skysail, Max would take him aside and give him little pointers on this duty or that, teach him the names of ropes (for the smallest rope had its own special name) and coach him on the "manners" of sailors when the ship was in port.

But for the most part, Herman Melville had little in common with his shipmates. They were all a good deal older than he, they were all lusty, hardened sailors who gave little thought to their souls, or when they did it was only to swear by a few superstitious beliefs. The first Sunday, when they reached the banks of Newfoundland on a cold, misty morning, he saw that it was no different from any other day aboard ship.

The sailors went around more moodily than usual because the weather was so damp; Jackson stayed in his bunk, snarling and groaning with rheumatism, now and again commanding one of the men to rub his back with arnica. Herman marveled at the way the rough sailors jumped to do the sordid, sick man's bidding; he beat a hasty retreat from the forecastle before *he* was ordered to do it. The raw, wet fogginess of the deck was preferable to the idea of touching so foul a creature as Jackson.

Wandering around, like a "sort of Ishmael in the ship," Herman came to the cook-house and peeped in the door. There the old black cook, who boiled such black coffee (or what was supposed to be coffee), and rarely stuck his head outside his small square of a kitchen, was sitting with his feet propped up on a shelf, reading the Bible. It was an ancient, worn and much grease-stained copy, and he was struggling to read the words, one by one, like the beginning readers in the country schoolroom at Sykes. "An' . . . de . . . Lawd . . . saith . . ." He looked up and noticed Herman. "Boy, can you read?" he asked.

Herman nodded, smiling.

"Then tell me wot dis mean," the cook demanded. He handed the Bible to Herman, marking the place with a greasy forefinger. It was a passage from the *Book of Chronicles,* one that had puzzled Herman as many passages puzzled him when he thought about them.

"That is a mystery no one can explain," he said, shaking his head as he handed back the Bible. "Not even the parsons."

But the old darkie could not be satisfied with that and went on, reading and figuring to himself. Herman left him and wandered off again. It was an aimless way to spend Sunday. He had grown so used to going to church that it seemed the thing to do and now he missed the meditation he found there. For several years now he had made use of the hours in church to develop his own philosophy—or try to; he was teeming with ideas deep inside him, but to form them into some sort of ordered pattern was another matter. It seemed to bring him closer to finding the answer to life, death and the hereafter merely to stand and gaze out over the ocean, or down into its unknown depths. But today the weather was so foggy you could hardly see over the side. It was indeed a gloomy Sunday.

He decided to descend into the forecastle again, but met Max coming up. The Dutchman was in a fit of anger. Jackson had set him to rubbing his back and then roundly cursed him because he did it too hard. Max had flown into a rage, told Jackson to rub his own back and left. "Don't you start doing vat he say, Boy," he advised Herman. "Then you never stop." He sighed.

"I'm trying to keep out of his way," Herman said. "But why do the men obey him? Why don't they tell the mates—or the captain?"

"It does no good to complain to de officers," Max said. "The forecastle belongs to de men, and what goes on down *dare,*" he pointed down the hatchway, "makes no difference to officers. In all merchant ships some sailor makes himself king of de forecastle, but I never see one like dis Jackson before." He shook his head and then shook a red, freckled fist in the air. "But one day we get him good. Wot you zay, Boy? You stand up and tell him to go to de devil?"

"Maybe," Herman considered. "But not for a while. Now I think it's better if I just keep out of his way."

"Yah, yah, I suppose. If he let you alone," muttered

the Dutchman. His eyes took on a gleam. "I know: vun
morning ve vill take charge of the burgoo, and let *him*
vait. Wot you zay to dat?"

"If you can get the rest to go along," Herman agreed.
It seemed petty, but sailors fought over petty things, and
Jackson, so full of evil, was really a petty tyrant. The
burgoo was a kind of symbol representing Jackson's rule
over all things.

The day drifted slowly by like the fog drifting slowly
around the ship. That night, as the larboard watch was
taking its turn to stay below from midnight till four and
Herman had just fallen into a sound sleep, they were
all startled by a terrible cry on deck. They tumbled out
of their bunks and up the hatchway in the darkness. The
whole ship's company went flying on deck. It was very
dark but they could see the mate, standing on the bowsprit, and crying out, "Luff! Luff!" a signal of danger.
They could just see a light, "and then, the great black hull
of a strange vessel that was coming down" on them, like
a monster looming up out of the ocean. It was so near
they could hear the topsails flap in the wind, the trampling
feet on the other deck and the mate of the strange ship
crying, "Luff! Luff!"

It was a terrifying moment. Herman caught his breath
as he heard "a snap and a crash, like the fall of a tree,
and suddenly one of the flying-jib guys jerked out the bolt
near the cathead," and in another minute they heard the
jib boom thumping against the bows. The strange ship
scraped by and passed into the darkness. It was a narrow
escape. They could breathe again, but they could not
sleep when they realized how close they had all come to
death. The accident had been caused by the drowsiness of
the lookouts on both ships, and the sailor who had been

lookout on the *St. Lawrence* was terribly reprimanded by the mate.

No wonder the night watches were so important, the lookout most of all. If the strange ship had come an inch closer, they would all have been killed. And the other ship must have been injured too, for when it grew light, there were pieces of strange rigging mixed with the *St. Lawrence.* The whole incident gave you an eerie feeling and brought out the dangers of the sea. It was a life of risk, and seafaring men took that risk for granted after a while. They lived on the edge of danger and thrived on it even. They were careless, trusting to luck to see them through. Mostly they gave the matter little thought. But Herman Melville thought about it the rest of the day, and often afterward. And he knew, if he were lookout, he would not let himself become drowsy. It was too important to stay awake.

Before the *St. Lawrence* left the banks of Newfoundland, a terrific storm fell upon it. The rain "poured down in sheets and cascades; the scupper holes could hardly carry it off the decks." And after the rain came a hard squall, which the sailors prepared for by "taking in canvas to double-reefed topsails." But even so, when the tornado finally came the motion of the ship was so violent that Herman could hardly stand on his feet. The others reeled about the deck, too, but they had been through such storms before and made light of it. They laughed at the stumbling of the new "boy," because making fun was part of their way of enduring the life. Jackson, however, more fiendish than the rest, started off a series of sarcastic remarks.

"Watch out the ship don't fall overboard!" he cackled in a loud voice above the wind and the rain. When his subjects roared with appreciation, adding a few shots of their own, he became nastier. "Why don't you get a hand-spike, Boy?" he asked, fixing his one good eye on Herman, like a snapping beetle, "and hold it down in the weather scuppers to steady the ship?"

But the new "boy" was catching on. "Why don't you do it?" he countered. "You're a better seaman!" And he made his way, in spite of the wild rocking, as far away from Jackson as he could stand.

Several of the sailors sniggered and Jackson told them to "shut their faces." He muttered, half to himself, "I'll teach that boy a lesson."

But Herman paid little attention to any of them. He could hardly catch his breath in the gale, to begin with, and the sailors' coarse, foolish talk was beginning to bore him. Life on a merchant ship certainly was far from glamorous. He clung to the rigging for dear life, wondering why he had ever come to sea.

But the storm passed, finally; and once it was over, they had fair weather till they got to the Irish Sea. Herman grew more skillful day by day in "running aloft" to reef the sails or loose them. After his first success in loosing the skysail, the mate decided he had the talent for becoming a real mariner; the duties of the chicken coop and pigsty were turned over to a Lancashire lad who preferred to stay on deck. It was a great relief to Herman, who soon became "as nimble as a monkey in the rigging." He was always among the first to "run aloft," and nothing delighted him more than to sit on one of the topsail-yards for hours, helping Max or the Greenlander as they worked at the rigging.

The first time he reefed the topsails on a dark night, hanging out over the yard with eleven others, with the ship plunging and rearing like a mad horse beneath them, his teeth chattered with trembling and he hung on tooth and nail to the spar. But after a few times he got used to it and was able to tie his reef knots as quickly as the best of the seamen, never making a "granny knot," the sailors' name for an incorrect one. And he learned to slip down on deck by the bare stays instead of the shrouds. Even Jackson had to admit grudgingly that the boy might have the makings of an able seaman.

One of the greatest thrills was furling the topgallant sails and royals in a hard blow, which required two hands on the yard. "There was a wild delirium about it; a fine rushing of the blood about the heart; and a glad thrilling and throbbing of the whole system, to find yourself tossed up at every pitch into the clouds of a stormy sky, and hovering like a judgment angel between heaven and earth; both hands free, with one foot in the rigging, and one somewhere behind you in the air. The sail would fill out like a balloon, with a report like a small cannon, and then collapse and sink away into a handful. And the feeling of mastering the rebellious canvas, and tying it down like a slave to the spar, and binding it over and over with the gasket, had a touch of pride and power in it. . . ." Herman Melville felt as if he had conquered a new world.

They would not let him steer much, except during a calm, when he had about as much to do as the figurehead on the bow. But at least he was at the helm, which was one of the latest kind—a system of cogs and wheels and spindles, all of polished brass, kept as shining as the brass at Grandmother Gansevoort's used to be. As each day passed, he realized that a sailor must be a jack-of-all-trades if he was really to master his calling—a seamstress, to darn and mend the sails; a ropemaker; a milliner, to tie graceful bows and knots; a blacksmith, to make hooks and thimbles, and even a bit of a musician, to sing out at the halyards. And though he still was not among the best, he was learning to give out with the strange chant with power and vigor.

There were some duties he did not enjoy, one of them pounding rust off the anchor: they would give him a club-hammer and swing him out over the bows in a bowline, and he would pound away for what seemed hours; it was monotonous work. And he still did not enjoy getting up at four in the morning, after the night watch of eight-to-twelve, but neither did the other sailors; they all grumbled and groaned as they tumbled out of their bunks. It was a rough life and a demanding one; but the fine feeling that came to him in being aloft made it all worth while.

The *St. Lawrence,* bearing her cargo, moved slowly across the Atlantic; it seemed as if they were not really bound for any port, but merely afloat on a boundless sea. And then one morning when Herman came up on deck, the sailors who were going below told him Ireland was in sight! They pointed toward the northeast, but when he rushed to the side all he could see was a bluish, cloudlike spot. Little by little it took the shape of a shoreline but it did not look so very different from the shoreline at home. Just what he had expected a foreign land to look like on first sight he did not know, but he was vaguely disappointed.

Then Wales came into view, but the mountains above the coastline looked amazingly like the Kaatskills along the Hudson. On the third day, with a good breeze, they came so near their destination that a pilot boat set to meet them, and the pilot came on board and began to order everyone about, just like the pilot who escorted them out of the Narrows.

"After running till about midnight, they *hove-to* near the mouth of the Mersey; and next morning, before daybreak, took the first of the flood; and with a fair wind, stood into the river. . . . Presently, in the misty twilight, they passed immense buoys, and caught sight of distant objects on shore, vague and shadowy shapes, like Ossian's ghosts." Herman stood leaning over the side, straining his eyes for the first sight of Liverpool. He could see a little, but the bell-buoy tolling in the harbor sounded an ominous welcome. As the day grew lighter the shadowy shapes took form, and when they finally came to anchor in the stream, still staring shoreward, he beheld a line of dingy warehouses all along the docks. It was like the warehouses along South Street in New York! He had come all the way across the Atlantic, and here was his reward!

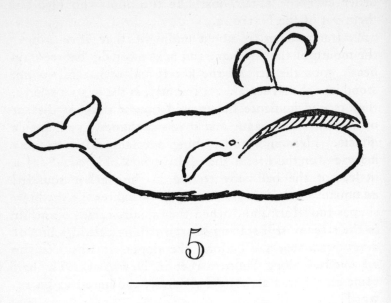

5

LIVERPOOL AND THE VOYAGE BACK

IT WAS NEARLY evening by the time the *St. Lawrence*
worked its way through a crowded harbor to a berth in
Prince's Dock, Liverpool. The crew was told to go ashore,
select boardinghouses and sit down to supper. (During
the time the ship was in dock, the men took their meals
ashore, as no fires were allowed on board. This meant
that the cook closed up the stove in the cook-house, much
to the sailors' delight.)

The men sprang ashore like prisoners freed for a holiday, and Herman Melville, eager to set foot on British
"soil," was among the first to rush down the gangplank;

but he felt the rough, bony hand of Jackson grabbing him by the shoulder. "Get back there, Boy!" His good eye snapped like a snake's. "Where d'ye think ye're goin'?" Without giving Herman a chance to answer, he took the lead. "*I* pick the place to go in port. Follow me, my fine hearties!" he called jeeringly over his shoulder. And the sailors obediently fell in line. Ashore or afloat, Jackson ruled their lives. His power was certainly puzzling, but Herman could not stop to figure it out then; he was too busy peering through the smoky darkness to see what it was possible to make out of this big, noisy industrial seaport.

Up one street and down another Jackson led them, till at last he brought them to a narrow lane, filled with boardinghouses and sailors. He stopped before the sign of the Baltimore Clipper. It was run by a broken-down American sailor and his English wife, Handsome Mary, as the men called her. She welcomed them like an old friend and led them to a private room where an enormous table was heaped with food for hungry sailors who had lived on nothing but salt beef and biscuit—sausages and beefsteaks and boiled potatoes and eggs and pickles and all kinds of food that Herman had almost forgotten the taste of. He dived in and ate as much as the huskiest of them; and while he ate he thought about the fact that he was seated in an English dining room, under an English roof, in an English tavern, part of the great English empire that he had read so much about in history books and heard his father speak about again and again. It was a staggering fact but it was true. And while he was here, he meant to look up some of the spots his father had visited. He had brought along the old guidebooks that he used to mull over in the house on Broadway and he was sure he could find the places from the directions.

The sailors slept on board ship. At daylight all hands were called and the decks were washed down. Then they had an hour to go ashore for breakfast, after which they worked at the rigging or some duty the mate thought up (for sailors must be occupied), and at twelve o'clock went to dinner. At one-thirty they were back at work, and finally "knocked off" at four in the afternoon. From that time on they were free to go where they pleased and, if they chose, were not required to be on board again till next morning at daylight to wash down the decks. If Herman was to do any sight-seeing, it had to be after four o'clock or on Sundays, which they had to themselves.

He could not do much in the late afternoon, and the first week he did not have his bearings well enough to wander very far from the section between the ship and the boardinghouse, where they took all their meals. But on the first Sunday in port, he took his old guidebook and started out. The first place he intended to see was the hotel where his father had stayed thirty years before. But when he came to the corner on which it was supposed to be, there was no sign of any hotel, and he learned from a bricklayer working near by that it had been pulled down many years ago. He went on to the next spot Mr. Melville had marked in the guidebook but that, too, was gone. Liverpool was an industrial city, rapidly growing and had no time to preserve its old buildings. In London, Herman might have seen Westminster Abbey and St. Paul's Cathedral and the Houses of Parliament, which had stood for so long and probably would stand for generations.

But he could not get to London, and though he walked the streets of Liverpool all day long, the only mark he found still present was a statue of Lord Nelson under a little archway in Chapel Street. He was terribly disappointed and tired by the time he got back to the Baltimore Clipper, where Handsome Mary gave him a cup of tea and tried to cheer him up.

None of the other sailors was interested in sight-seeing; they knew Liverpool backward and forward and came ashore for fun. They went to the taverns, to the cheap music halls and dingy gambling houses. Herman was left to shift for himself, and one of the most interesting sights to him was the great line of docks which proved not to be like New York docks at all, but solid structures of stone, like the China wall. Here were ships from the Far East, too—from China and India and Malaya. Sometimes he boarded the ships to see what they were like; they had the flavor of distant lands about them, curious designs and exotic cargoes. Poking around the docks made him feel, more than anything the sailors might show him, that he had traveled a long way and was in touch with the remote parts of the globe.

He saw, too, in wandering about by himself through the soot-filled streets, the squalor and hopelessness of real poverty. His mother's house by the river at home, pinched as it was, seemed like a palace compared to the dreary tenements huddled together in the sordid alleys of Liverpool. He was only nineteen but he felt outraged at a civilization that could be so unjust as to allow poverty like that to exist in the midst of thriving commerce.

One day as he was passing through an alley called "Launcelott's-Hey," he heard a low moan coming from what seemed to be a crack in the sidewalk. Not a soul was in sight. Then he saw that there was an opening between the cellars of two warehouses; looking down he saw, some fifteen feet below the sidewalk, the shrunken figure of a starving woman, her arms folded around two children. At first he thought they were all dead, but again the wail came from the vault. He ran to get help, but the policeman he asked said that "was not his block," and he could do nothing about it. Nobody would help the wretched creatures. Herman managed to get some water and a little food to them, but the children were too weak to do more than drink the water and the woman did not move. The next day when he came to help them it was the same, and on the third day all three were dead. When he left the ship at noon, he hurried to Launcelott's-Hey, and the vault was empty. "In place of the woman and children, a heap of quick-lime was glistening." The police, who would not help, had removed and covered up the signs of the suffering.

It was an incident Herman Melville never forgot, and it made him realize the thoughtlessness of men, the cruelty they showed toward each other. As he walked alone through the streets of Liverpool during his off-hours, he pondered on the evil in the world in contrast to the good that the churches tried to teach, and he knew that he must one day put his thoughts on paper and do what he could to make men see. Right now he was a lonely and disappointed young man, and he wrote to his mother that he would "give all the sights of Liverpool to see a corner of home," although he had been so glad in many ways to leave home. Beggars appeared to be everywhere —along the dock walls, trying to salvage anything that could be used in the discarded trash of the ships; in the "booble-alleys," or boardinghouse streets, trying to sell or beg or sing a few coins out of the "prosperous" sailors. Every street had its strolling musicians whose songs mingled with the noisy shouts and brawls of women and children. Nothing could have been further from what he had expected.

And in the wealthier parts of town away from the docks, Herman could see nothing very different from New York or Albany. More and more he wondered why he had been so anxious to see England.

But the next Sunday was a beautiful day in July and in the morning, with a lunch in his pocket, he left the dingy streets of the city and walked toward the headlands above the sea. Soon he was high up, "commanding a wide sweep of view"; meadows, woodland and green hedge was all around him. The air was soft and dewy and seemed "tinged with the green of the grass." At last he had found old England—in the country! Walking on, he came to a little church with an ivy-covered porch, just like the pictures of English churches he had seen in the portfolio prints at home. He went in and stayed through the service; and though the people stared at him a little because he was strange, they accepted him and made him welcome. After church he continued his ramblings and came to an inn with tables out under an apple tree where people were leisurely sipping ale out of mugs. The "host" of the inn invited him to sit down, and three friendly young men talked to him and treated him to a mug of ale.

Toward sundown, when he was on the way back to town, he came upon a charming cottage; a farmer and his wife were sitting outside the door and their three young daughters were hanging out of the window which was covered with roses. It was indeed "just like the pictures"! What was more, the farmer insisted that he stop for a bowl of milk and bade one of his pretty daughters fetch it. Herman stayed till the sun was almost set and came back to Liverpool feeling that he had found England after all.

And the next Sunday he found a friend. For several days, he had seen a young fellow about his own age hanging around the boardinghouses, just watching the sailors as they came and went. But on Sunday the boy was at the Baltimore Clipper when Herman came there for supper and he was asking the Greenlander about passage to America. He was a good-looking young man, of good education from his speech, with an interesting manner, an air that gave an impression of something out of the ordinary in his life.

As the Greenlander did not offer much information, Herman spoke up. "I'll be glad to tell you anything you want to know about America," he offered.

The young man whose name was Henry Gill, looked him over curiously for a moment but then asked, "Why don't we go for a walk?" So they rambled about St. George's Pier until nearly midnight that night, talking about everything under the sun.

It was good to have someone you could talk to once more! Before they parted for the night, "Harry" had confided many facts about himself. How he had been left a modest fortune when his parents died; how he had gone through it when he became of age and had shipped to India as a midshipman in the British navy; how he had made two or three voyages, but was disgusted with the service; how he had come back to his home in rural England, but was bored and decided he wanted to see America. It was for this reason he had come to Liverpool, but now that he was here he had suddenly hit upon the idea of going to the new country as a sailor instead of a pas-

senger and that was why he had been haunting the board-inghouses.

As soon as he heard that his new friend wanted to ship as a sailor, Herman suggested, "Why don't you sign on the *St. Lawrence?* Three of the men deserted a few days ago and I know Captain Brown will be glad to sign you up." He was thinking how nice it would be to have a real friend on board, one who spoke his language.

"I'll do it!" agreed Harry. And the next morning he appeared on the *St. Lawrence* before Captain Brown, who agreed to take him on as a "boy," since he had had no experience on a merchant ship.

Herman warned him that the good captain, who seemed so interested in his career, would not be so friendly once they were at sea. He also told his new shipmate all about Jackson and cautioned him to be careful of Jackson's rascally temper, his tyranny and hatred, particularly of those who would not bow to him.

Harry listened with wide-open eyes. He had seen a good bit of the world, but he had not come across a character like Jackson's and he wondered if the story weren't a little exaggerated. For his part, it made Herman feel like an old hand to be giving advice and pointers to a new recruit. He hadn't realized how much he had learned about sailors and the sea during the voyage out. He was in many ways "experienced" though he had only his initial voyage behind him.

He now had a companion in his strolls through Liver-pool every afternoon and the city took on a different air. It was not quite so bleak nor seemed so unfriendly. And on Sundays the two would take off for the country right after breakfast to explore the land on every side. Harry was a generous and entertaining fellow; he sold some of his remaining valuables for cash, so their jaunts could include all the fun that was to be had along the way. And he kept up a running fire of conversation about his adventures among the lords and ladies he had run around with in London, the racy people among whom he had lost his inheritance. Sometimes Herman suspected that not all the stories were from Harry's own memories, but they were colorful and fascinating, so he would not bother about the truth of them. A tall tale was a joy in itself.

The first week in August, the *St. Lawrence* was "advertised to sail in two days' time," and on the sixth, the ship set sail with three new hands to man her sails, one of them Herman's friend Harry, who looked forward to the voyage as a new high adventure. The departure was a sight that might well make him feel he was off to a great wide world; there had been a breeze blowing up the river which had held a good many ships in dock for the past four days. So that "there was now under weigh, a vast fleet of merchantmen, all steering broad out to sea. The white sails glistened in the clear morning air like a great Eastern encampment of sultans; and from many a forecastle came the deep mellow old song 'Ho-o-he-yo, cheerily men!' as the crews catted their anchors. The wind was fair; the weather mild; the sea most smooth."

Herman's friend leaned over the side admiring the scene, until the mate bellowed, "And what might ye be? A cabin passenger? Get to work, Boy!" And he set him to coiling ropes. The other sailors looked at him more disdainfully than they had at Herman the first few days of the voyage out; Harry was too dandified to suit them. They were not only contemptuous of him but suspicious as well. Why would such a fine young well-educated man ship as a common sailor? His hands were much too white, his clothes, those they could glimpse when he opened the large mahogany chest he had brought aboard, were much too fancy.

The sailors were especially suspicious of the chest. It was such fine wood and ornamented by brass screw heads, altogether too elegant for the rough quarters below deck. The men were positive that Harry was running away from justice, that he had been part of a gambling ring in London and had had to escape to sea to avoid being thrown into jail. Both Max the Dutchman and the Greenlander confided their suspicions to Herman and would not listen when he tried to tell them they were wrong. Jackson made all kinds of sneering remarks.

Things looked bad for Harry from the first day but what made it worse, and what puzzled Herman the most, was the way his friend avoided "running aloft" when an order was given. He would suddenly be very busy coiling away the slack of the rigging about the decks until his shipmates had sprung into the shrouds. Or he would make the clew lines fast to the belaying pin with such ardor that he would be too late to mount over the bulwarks before the others got there. Once they had already started up, he would pretend to hurry into the shrouds and appear quite put out that the others had beat him to it.

Herman finally spoke to him about it; and then the truth came out: Harry had tried privately and found out he simply could not go aloft; he got dizzy, his nerves went to pieces and he couldn't stand the strain.

"But your two voyages to Bombay—you must have gone aloft then!" Herman burst out. He could not understand his friend.

But Harry colored and said he had got out of it some way; Herman couldn't tell if he was telling the truth

or if he had made the whole story up—being a midshipman, going to India and all the rest of it. Harry had an
imagination which carried him away, certainly; and this
time it had led him into a serious situation.

"Harry, you were mad to ship," he said solemnly. He
gave him some idea of what it would be like when the
mate discovered his fear, of the way their shipmates
would taunt and torture him. "The only way to gain any
respect from them is by running aloft at the first order."
He jumped into the rigging and began to climb. Since he
felt that running aloft and being up in the sky among
the topmost sails was the best part of becoming a sailor,
he couldn't believe that Harry would not feel the same
once he had made it to the top. "Try again," he urged.
"Perhaps you only imagine it; and pretty soon you'll be
right at home among the spars, like a bird in a tree."

But Harry only shook his head obstinately. "I *can't.*"
For once the words did not flow from his lips.

"Well, one of these days the mate will realize what's
going on and you'll have to go aloft, whether you can
or not," Herman warned him.

And sure enough, the mate singled him out one morning and commanded him to mount to the main-truck and
unreeve the short signal halyards. Harry only stared at
him, aghast.

"Away you go!" said the mate, snatching a whip's end.

Poor Harry was frightened out of his wits and called
out for Captain Brown, but the mate laughed at him and
laid the rope across his back. "Take that, and along with
you!" He flourished the rope again. "Up you go!"

Harry looked round at the grinning tars with a glance
of terrible indignation and agony. He sought Herman's
eye despairingly for some kind of help. The young mar-

iner wanted to help his friend who had proved such a
weakling, but he knew that if he intervened it would
merely mean more trouble for both of them. He nodded
his head slightly by way of encouragement and as a signal
to obey.

Seeing that there was no hope, Harry made one bound
into the rigging and was up at the maintop in a trice. A
few more springs would take him to the truck. But no;
he stopped short and looked down from the top. It was
fatal. Herman saw him reel and clutch at the shrouds,
till the mate shouted out, "Don't squeeze the tar out of
the ropes. Up you go, sir."

But Harry was frozen to the maintop. Herman longed
to help him, but the mate sent Max the Dutchman up
instead. Max was at the top in no time, and butted Harry
like a redheaded goat up the rest of the way, step by step.
At last he gained the royal yard, and the thin signal halyards were flying in the wind.

"Unreeve!" cried the mate.

Harry's arm stretched out—his legs seemed shaking in
the rigging, even to those on deck; and at last, thank
heaven! the deed was done! Herman breathed a sigh of
relief for his friend. But when Harry came down, he was
pale as death, with bloodshot eyes and quivering in every
limb. It had been too much for him.

He vowed he would never set foot in the rigging again
and even petitioned the mate to let him become a steerage
passenger; he would pay his fare when he got to America
and sold some of his finery. But the mate would not hear
of it; Harry had signed on as a sailor and a sailor he
must be till the end of the voyage. He was put in charge
of cleaning the longboat and the chicken coops and all
the menial tasks that Herman had so hated. But he would

do anything rather than go aloft.

From then on he led a miserable life at the hands of the other sailors who jeered and jibed at him constantly, in spite of all Herman tried to do to shield him. It was strange; Harry had seemed such a man of the world in Liverpool, so full of dash and secret daring; and now he was reduced to a mincing boy. While Herman Melville on the other hand now seemed strong and experienced, as hearty and brave as any of the *St. Lawrence* crew. He still was not of their kind, but they all had great respect for a young sailor, still a boy, who ran aloft at the first bidding and could loose or reef a sail with the dexterity of a seasoned hand.

Only Jackson retained his attitude of resentment toward Herman. It was almost as if he hated Herman for being so quietly efficient and skillful. And part of his hatred arose out of the fact that he was growing weaker and sicker all the time, so that he had to remain in his bunk—he, who prided himself on being the best seaman. He became more tyrannical than ever and abused the whole crew right and left. When the sailors' tobacco ran low, he divided and rationed it out, though he himself had an ample supply which he shared with no one. When a sailor refused to rub his back he flew into such a rage and heaped such vile curses on the man, that his mates drew back in horror. Sailors were superstitious and curses were a cause for fear.

Finally the whole situation got so intolerable that one night during the dogwatch, Max put it up to the group who were standing around the windlass to rebel against Jackson in some way that would show him that sick or well, he could not rule their lives. (The men had just been listening to Harry sing an old country air; they discovered that in spite of his "yellow" streak, he had a voice, one day when he "sang out" at a rope, and from then on they forgave him his cowardly nerves if he would favor them with a song.)

But when he stopped, Max started his own sad lament on Jackson's treatment of him that morning at breakfast when he had stuck in his spoon out of turn while they were devouring the burgoo, which had come down a bit later than usual. They were all hungry from washing down the deck and it was hard to wait your turn. He had been wrong, but he did not deserve the abuse Jackson heaped upon his red head. Even now his face grew redder, his mustaches more fiery in the moonlight as he recalled Jackson's mockery and his discipline, making Max wait till all the rest had finished.

"Dat old devil!" The Dutchman shook his fist in the direction of the forecastle. "He sit down dare, on his bunk, coughing curses at us like a yellow Satan."

"Aye, aye," agreed several of the sailors. The Greenlander put his hands over his ears. "Never I hear such language. In my country he could be sued."

"I say ve should teach him a lesson!" Max brought his fist down on the windlass. "You, Melville, you remember vat we said about taking de kid in de morning? Tomorrow we do it? Vat you zay?"

But Herman felt a strange pity for Jackson, in spite of the man's evil soul. The veteran sailor was so ill, as if his own venom were eating him up inside. It was somehow pathetic. "I don't know," he said slowly. "I think Jackson is getting punished for his sins in his coughing fits and bleeding spells."

"They only make him meaner toward us," cried another sailor who had recently come under Jackson's fire.

"I say Max is right!"

"Aye, Max is right," joined in one or two more.

"Goot!" cried Max, clapping his big red palms together. "Now my plan is, in de morning, ven de burgoo comes down. . . ." He drew the men together and spoke in a low whisper, outlining the scheme he had suggested to Herman on the voyage out. The men looked rather doubtful but finally agreed to try it. Word was passed around to the sailors on the other watch, so they would all be prepared. A few of them opposed the plan but the ringleaders stood firm.

The next morning when the long black arm of the cook handed down the kid of burgoo and the can of molasses, Max the Dutchman was at the bottom of the hatchway to take it. But instead of passing it along to Jackson, who sat cross-legged on his bunk waiting to do the honors as usual, Max sat down on the forecastle ladder, put the kid between his knees as Jackson always did and began to pour in the molasses himself, utterly ignoring the old sailor. No one spoke. The men stood around, watching warily, not daring to look at Jackson except out of the corners of their eyes, as if they didn't notice anything unusual in the proceedings.

"All right," said Max, when he had finished making a "dismal swamp" of molasses in the burgoo, "bring your spoons and get in line, hearties!"

The men stared at each other, still not able to face Jackson, but each wanting some one of the others to start. The silence was stifling. At last one of the men who had joined in with Max went up and put in his spoon. Two or three more started to form in line behind him, but at that moment Jackson leaped like a yellow tomcat off his bunk, his good eye, and even his bad one, snapping with rage. Pushing aside the other sailors, he stood squarely in front of Max, his aches and pains forgotten in his anger.

"Well, Max," he said with deadly sarcasm, "I see you have taken over my duties for me. How very kind of you, since I am so ill." He gave a hoarse cackle. "That's why you're doing it, of course."

The Dutchman did not have the courage to come out with the true reason. "Vy, sure—ve all zay, you are zo zick . . ." He had no chance to finish.

Jackson's clawlike hands snatched the kid from between Max's knees, and he let out a roaring oath. "I'm not that 'zick'!" He raised the container of burgoo high over his head and turned it upside down over Max's as he brought it down. The burgoo, which luckily was never too hot from the cook-house, streamed heavily down the Dutchman's face and clothes, making a ridiculous and sorry figure out of a rebellious one. The sailors, particularly those who always fawned on Jackson, let out loud hysterical guffaws, snorts and stomps. But the tyrant was not satisfied. He hurled the can of molasses against the side of the forecastle, near where Herman was standing with his friend Harry, so that it spattered down the wall and all over both of them. "You two had something to do with this!" he roared more hoarsely now. His voice was almost rasping. "Boys always make trouble for me —until they learn that I'll run this forecastle—till the day I die!" With that he began to cough so violently and so long that the sailors thought he was going to die right then; but finally, grabbing hold of one of them for support, he hobbled back to his bunk, suddenly spent and shrunken.

Herman said calmly to Harry, who was trembling with

astonishment and fright, "We'd better wash this stuff off our clothes." He neither looked at Jackson nor made any reply. "You come, too, Max."

The three of them got water from the scuttle-butt and made themselves as presentable as possible. Herman said nothing to Max about the miserable failure of his plan; one look at the Dutchman's face when he had washed it clean of cornmeal was enough. Later he learned that Max apologized to Jackson and tried to make a joke of it all. But Herman kept silent toward all of them except Harry. He had no reason to apologize to Jackson and felt no need to do so. And surprisingly enough, the old sailor left him alone for the rest of the voyage. What was more, once his terrible anger had been let loose, Jackson had time to think of the cause of the outburst against him. Perhaps he had gone too far. He let up in his nagging and needling of the sailors, told a few more stories and cracked a few jokes now and then. After all, he needed them more than they needed him. He might not be able to subdue them a second time.

Max was pleased with even such meager results from his "mutiny," but the young mariner from New York shook his head over the behavior of sailors. The mysterious power of a man like Jackson would always be a puzzle to him.

Several weeks later, toward the end of September, the steward, coming off the quarter-deck one noon after Captain Brown had taken his observations with the quadrant, announced to all the ship: "Off Cape Cod!"

Off Cape Cod! In the "shore-bloom" that came with the words, Herman thought he could smell the hay in the barn at Broadhall again, or the roses his mother had cut from their little garden in the house by the river a few days before he left home. All the land sights and smells of home were in those words.

At first the *St. Lawrence* ran into a stiff breeze and then into a deadly calm. It was Sunday and "the midday sun shone upon a glassy sea." They could see the shores of New Jersey but they could not reach them. "The sailors whistled and whistled for a wind. . . ." And "presently, up came a dainty breeze, wafting a white wing from the shore—the pilot boat!"

The next morning they set sail for the Narrows and, by making short tacks, at last ran through, almost bringing the jib boom over one of the forts. Then the city of New York rose out of the bay, its spires piercing the blue. To Herman Melville, the port he had seen and loved all his life never looked so enchanting as it did that day.

"Hurra! hurra! and ten thousand times hurra! Down goes our old anchor, fathoms down into the free and independent Yankee mud. . . ." he sang deep in his heart as the anchor dropped into the river.

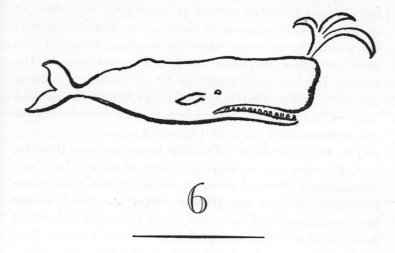

6

HOME AGAIN

THAT NIGHT the two boys, having no place to stay ashore, slept on board the *St. Lawrence* and had the pleasure of a quiet forecastle all to themselves. (The other sailors had rushed ashore as soon as the ship docked.) The ship they both had loathed at times seemed peaceful and friendly now, and it was good to know you could spend all night in, without being roused in the middle of the best sleep to go on deck for the next watch.

In the morning, Captain Brown settled accounts with the crew for their four months of service. The men stood lined up in his cabin while he handed out their pay, one by one. As boys, Herman Melville and Henry Gill were left until the very last, and then the captain managed to cheat them out of their full wages, little as those were. He charged Herman almost as much for "expenses" in Liverpool as the amount of his whole wages for the voyage and deducted some more for two hammers that had been lost while Herman was pounding the rust off the anchor. He had hardly enough to get home on, after a summer's labor! Harry fared just as badly, for he had received a month's advance before they left Liverpool and now collected the grand sum of $1.50.

The two friends left the ship in disgust and indignation. Herman felt he must get home at once to see how his mother's financial affairs were going, and Harry accompanied him to the Hudson River steamboat where they said good-by. Harry was going to look for a job as a clerk; he had had enough of the life of a sailor. And as the little steamboat chugged up the Hudson toward Albany, Herman felt almost the same way. His first voyage had proved a disappointment on so many counts; only the wonderful exhilaration he felt from riding the sea high up in the shrouds when he ran aloft to carry out an order or, better still, when he sat on one of the topsail yards and watched the sea below and the sky above glide past—only those moments had made the sailor's life worthwhile. But maybe that was enough; certainly it was an experience he would always cherish. (And it was the very thing that made his friend run from the sea like a rabbit. Herman smiled to himself. How different one human being was from another!)

At home the family were all glad to see him—his small brother Tom, now nine and a half, had a million questions to ask about the sea—but poor Mrs. Melville was in worse straits than ever. Her debts had run up so high she was going to have to sell some of the furniture to pay them.

"Allan is working in Albany again," she told Herman once the excitement of his homecoming was over and they sat down to take stock of family affairs. "But he needs all he earns for his keep. And Gansevoort needs all the strength he has to study law."

"I know." Herman nodded. He had not stopped to see Gansevoort in New York because he was worried about his mother's affairs from the letters she had sent while he was away.

Augusta spoke up. "I would be willing to become a governess, but mother won't hear of it."

"Certainly not!" Mrs. Melville silenced her with authority.

"Mother won't even hear of us taking in sewing," said Helen. "She thinks it would be undignified." (Kathy and Priscilla, at thirteen and eleven, still felt too young to voice an opinion. With Tom, they sat wide-eyed at their older brother's feet.) "After all, it's 1839," Helen continued. "Times are changing."

"No female of a genteel family goes to work," Mrs. Melville said firmly. "I have written a letter to Uncle Peter asking him for a fixed sum of $50 a month. I suppose you will want to see him and Allan, Herman; you can take the letter when you go. In the meantime," she went on expectantly, "I hope you have brought us something from your summer abroad." (She said it as if he had been making the grand tour.)

Then the young mariner had to tell them how unprofitable his summer had actually been. He gave his mother the little he had left, and they all sympathized with him on the hard-heartedness of Captain Brown, but he couldn't help feeling that he had failed them some way. Except for little Tom, it was a dismal family circle he had rushed home to see. A few days later, he took the letter to Uncle Peter in Albany twenty miles away, and when he left he carried Uncle Peter's check for $50— but with an answer saying that that could not be a "fixed sum" every month.

On the way home, he stopped at some of the villages along the Hudson to inquire about teaching school again. He felt he must do something, and quickly, although it was hardly likely that the number of openings for teachers would be any greater now than when he had gone away in June. To his surprise, however, they did need a teacher, or supervisor, at the Greenbush and Schodack Academy, in the village of Greenbush, thirteen miles from Lansingburgh. He would have to pay board during the week, but he could walk home every Saturday for the week end, which would cut his expenses. His first quarter's salary would have to go for board and some new clothes, but after that he figured he could allow his mother between $150 and $200 a year. Maybe Allan would soon be able to send something. The prospects suddenly looked brighter.

He started teaching before the end of October. He was more at ease now in facing his pupils, a group of sixty, twice the number he had had at Sykes. But he knew from his first experience how to handle the boys who needed discipline; he was a year older now and the summer at sea made him look more than that. He was sunburned, windburned and muscular. His small blue eyes were bluer because of his tawny skin; they were reflective but pene-

trating. He was not easily fooled and would accept no
nonsense, but he was not a dictator or a tyrant in a classroom. His students liked and respected him.

However, the school at Greenbush had no more to keep
it going than the one at Sykes, and by the following May,
Herman Melville was once more out of a job and wondering once again what he could do to earn a living. There
was a serious depression all over the country, but perhaps along the frontier it wasn't felt as much as in the
east. He began to think about Uncle Thomas out in
Galena, and the more he thought about it the better he
liked the idea of going west to try his luck.

He confided his scheme to a friend he had made at
Greenbush—Eli Fly, who was also at loose ends looking
for something to do. Neither one had enough money to
travel, either by train or boat, but the lack of funds didn't
stop them. Herman had another idea: they could work
their way out west along the bustling Erie Canal—they
would be "canallers" for a summer, part of the crew of
picturesque, swaggering, vagabond adventurers who went
from city to city across the 360 miles of New York State
by manning the barges and boats that carried goods and
passengers back and forth.

The life of the canallers was wild and unruly. The
crew changed at every port, because there were always
two or three who decided to try their luck at one of the
cities along the way. There was a great deal of rough
work to be done, without the glamor of seagoing ships
nor the mystery and wonder of the sea. But the two who
set out from Albany were congenial companions, and both
were interested in seeing some of the country they had
heard about—western New York, Pennsylvania and
Ohio.

The scenery was constantly changing. Big cities like Buffalo would be followed by long stretches of dismal, uninhabited swamps. Then they would pass thriving villages and rich, cultivated fields, bursting with crops. Then through deep forests on either side of the canal and under Roman arches across Indian rivers. It was a revelation to both Herman and his friend to find that their country offered so many different kinds of land along its broad expanse.

"I always had the notion that all of the United States was just like the east, except for the Indians," Eli laughed one day as they drew alongside a landing at a small settlement near Cleveland.

Herman nodded, smiling. "And how many people in Greenbush or Lansingburgh, do you suppose, have any idea how great in size the Great Lakes are? They're really fresh-water seas!" He was surprised at the expanse of water that was Lake Erie, at the roughness of the waves that had sunk many a square-sail brig or three-masted ship as well as the canoes and open boats that ventured out from its banks.

Cleveland itself was another surprise—and a pleasant one. The inviting harbor, wide clean streets, all paved, and the variety of new buildings—quite as impressive as the state buildings in Albany—were an unexpected sight so far out west. In Cleveland they heard of a steamer that would take them through the lakes to Chicago for $10. They decided to take the money they had earned as canallers and travel as passengers the rest of the way.

The night they left, one of the sudden electrical storms that made even the best of sailors fear Lake Erie, blew up out of nowhere, chopping up the water so that the wood-burning steamboat heaved and tossed all night like

a birch canoe and even the horses on board were seasick. Poor Eli was sure that if they weren't drowned in a sinking ship, he would be dead by morning anyhow, but Herman convinced him it would all be over when the storm passed. The young mariner found that his experience on the high seas stood him in good stead now; he was not seasick and he was not afraid. But the storm was as bad as the one he had been through on the *St. Lawrence,* and there were moments when the lightning flashed, the boat heeled crazily and the passengers screamed, so that he wondered if they would survive the terrible upheaval.

But by morning it was calm again, and when they came on deck they saw the islands around Point Pelee gleaming like jewels in the sunshine. It was hard to believe they had been in a howling tempest all night long. The two young men stood at the rail and took in the romantic sight—the fishing boats, the green shores, the blue water—and both of them felt it was good to be alive.

Detroit was disappointing. It was noisy and dirty, full of sharpshooters trying to work their schemes on the immigrants who poured in by rail and ship. The city was becoming a railroad center instead of a fur-trading post, not nearly so interesting to the two young travelers as it would have been a few years earlier. From Detroit they crossed Lake St. Clair and then moved up the St. Clair River, where they passed sailing vessels, and were raced by Indians, who set out from their wigwams along the shore to see if they could overtake the steamboats and peddle their fur pelts.

Lake Huron seemed to be bounded by a vast wilderness. No signs of life except the occasional shack of a summer woodchopper who furnished the fuel for steamers —nothing but dark masses of trees, "ancient and un-entered forests," Herman thought to himself. It gave you a weird feeling to think of those hundreds of miles of black forest, uninhabited except by wild life.

But after a while the dark line of trees shifted and the shoreline showed rocks and high cliffs, which meant they were approaching Fort Mackinac and Mackinac Island. From the deck of the lake boat, the fort looked like a huge white monument built on the heights, while 300 feet below it clustered the houses of the town and the wigwams of different tribes of Indians lining the beach. Herman learned from the captain that they would have time to explore the island, so the two friends went first to the old fort, where they wandered through the ruins, re-calling the stories of history books which told of the fort and the battles that took place there.

Going down the cliffs, they came into the little town where more than half of the people they saw were Indians —Ojibways, Menominees and the wild Winnebagos from the west, one of the missionaries told Herman. (The missionaries of the French church showed travelers around the town in the hope of getting a contribution for their work among the Indians.)

From Mackinac, the steamer chugged down the shore of deep blue Lake Michigan ("the land of the sky-blue water," the Indians called it), and then crossed over to the new settlement named Milwaukee where a good many of the passengers, who had decided to try the town with the Indian name, left the boat. By the time it arrived in Chicago, only about half of the number who started out from Cleveland were still on board.

Chicago, only seven years old in the summer of 1840, was the biggest, most bustling town in the west; warehouses lined the streets back of the docks already, to store the goods that poured in, and hotels lined the main streets to house the travelers that poured in. It was like an overgrown adolescent, bulging with muscle power long before becoming of age. Neither of the young men from the banks of the Hudson cared to linger in the confusion longer than necessary, so the next day they set out on horseback (the cheapest way they could find) across the prairies west of Chicago toward Galena.

For three days they rode through the tall grasses which sometimes came as high as their saddles, and just now, in early July, were covered with flowers—all colors, purple, yellow, red and blue waving in the wind—so that they felt as if they were riding through a sea of color. It was a strange sensation. The second day they crossed fields of striped tiger lilies which fairly danced in front of their eyes, while the horses "waded" knee-deep among the stalks. They spoke little crossing those fields; the countryside was lonely and deserted except for the flowers, which created a spell like the legends one read about fields of poppies that put people to sleep. Years later Herman remembered the scene vividly when he wrote down his impression of it for all time.

They found Uncle Thomas' house in Galena by asking one of the settlers on the main street—there were only 2000 in the village and Thomas Melville was the notary public. He also was commissioner of deeds for settlers from Massachusetts and Maine, and he collected real estate taxes as an official in the chamber of commerce. But in spite of these high-sounding positions, he had as little if not less to live on than in Pittsfield. The house in Galena, overflowing with children, was a cheese box compared to a mansion like Broadhall. Uncle Thomas himself looked worn out with care and, for the first time, wrinkled with age. His hair had always been gray as far as Herman could remember, but until now his uncle's face had been smooth.

"You see I've not been much more successful here than I was in Pittsfield." He smiled, took a pinch of snuff and shrugged his shoulders, as Herman had seen him do so many times. "I guess I wasn't cut out to be a businessman any more than a farmer. It's hard to say what the Melville talents are, my boy. My Tom took to the sea, but he's in trouble half the time. What about you?"

Herman smiled in turn. "I didn't get into much trouble after the first few days; and I think I have talent as a foretopman. I like being a sailor when you're above deck, above the sweat and grind of dirty jobs." He hesitated, but went on rather shyly, "I also like to write."

"And do you have talent for that?" his uncle asked skeptically.

Herman did not answer for a long moment. His eyes took on the distant light which had disturbed his shipmates because it set him apart from them. Then, like his uncle, he shrugged his shoulders. "I have imaginings," he said. "Whether they come from the gods, or what may come out of them, I cannot tell yet."

There was little or nothing Uncle Thomas could do for Herman or his friend. The depression had hit the little towns in the west as well as the east. Schools were closed, banks had no need of clerks and even farming seemed to be at a standstill. By the middle of August, both young men realized they were not going to find jobs and decided to head back east.

Going home, they boarded the river boat on the Mississippi to St. Louis, where they visited the Indian mounds. The flat banks of the wide river were like tow paths on either side. It might almost have been a canal except that it was so broad. Here, too, were Indians, frontiersmen in leather suits, theatrical people in showboats and every conceivable kind of sharpshooter selling medicine, trinkets or real estate to the tourists. The river boats and the life on the river were one continual show.

At the junction of the Muskingum and Ohio, they left the boat and started out across the Alleghenies, doing a day's work here and there along the way to earn enough to take them to the next town. By the middle of November they reached New York, with a few dollars in their pockets and a summer of interesting, varied impressions in their memories. Years later, Herman made use of these, but at the moment, when he and Eli descended on Gansevoort in New York, his older brother saw a pair of young, irresponsible, dusty wayfarers who were only another problem. He was still not feeling too well, trying to study law with funds from Judge Lemuel Shaw, an old friend of their father, and he was not much in sympathy with the two who had just spent such a lackadaisi-

cal, harum-scarum three months. Nevertheless, he paid
for their dinners every night and kept a watchful eye on
Herman, all the time urging both boys to look for work.

But by the end of November nothing had turned up for
either one, and he wrote to Allan: "Herman is still here—
He has been and is a source of great anxiety to me—He
has not obtained a situation—Fly is still on the lookout—
He has so far been unsuccessful. They are both in good
health and tolerable spirits—and are living at a cheap
rate, $2.50 per week, exclusive of dinner. They dine with
me every day at Sweeney's and are blessed with good ap-
petites—as my exchequer can vouch—Herman has had
his hair sheared and whiskers shaved and looks more like
a Christian than usual—" Indeed, he wondered privately
how much of a "Christian" his younger brother could be,
with his odd notions, his constant wanderlust and his lack
of ambition.

Herman spent far too much time reading novels, in
Gansevoort's opinion. What sort of "study" was that?
But Herman Melville felt a kinship with writers of stories
that went deep into his being, and he read avidly with the
same thirst for a knowledge of story making that Gansevoort had for law making. One of the new books he devoured between-times while he was job hunting, was *Two
Years Before the Mast,* by Richard Henry Dana, Jr.,
which had just been published. As he read, he was struck
by the "strange, congenial feelings" he had toward the
author of the gripping novel. It might almost have been
he, Herman Melville, who was telling the tale of life at
sea; and it made him long to try his luck in a different
direction—to sail the blue Pacific, to see for himself what
lay beyond the horizons you could see from eastern
shores.

Early in December, Eli came back to the boarding-house one day with the news that he had a position as a copyist and, while the two friends celebrated with an extra-large dinner at Sweeney's, (still at the expense of poor Gansevoort, who could never eat much) Eli urged Herman to try for a job at the same firm. "We could work together and next summer we can take another trip together," he said. "There's still plenty of this country to be seen."

Herman agreed to try, although his mind was already half made up to follow the sea once more. He applied for the copyist's job the next day but his handwriting was not good enough, the employer said. He was not sorry; he could hardly picture himself spending the rest of his days at a desk, or even a part of his days, at his age. He was twenty-one, strong, eager to live and to think on his own. The life of an office worker was not for him!

He thought of Richard Dana's rich retelling of life in the Pacific; he thought of all the places his cousin Thomas had been. And he heard of a brand new whaling vessel, the *Acushnet,* sailing from New Bedford by the end of December. He confided his plans to Gansevoort in the end, because he needed his older brother's help in carrying them out. On a very cold day between Christmas and New Year's, the two brothers came to New Bedford and before another week Herman had embarked on his latest, and greatest, adventure.

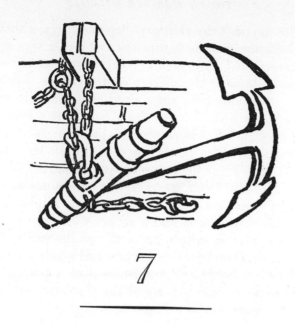

7

THE YOUNG MARINER JOINS A
WHALING CREW

A WHALING VOYAGE, Herman Melville discovered from his first day out, was different as the night from day when compared to his first voyage on the *St. Lawrence*. A merchant ship merely transported cargo from one point on the globe to another. A whaler set out across the oceans to seize its cargo—stalk it, capture it and reduce it to a form and size that could be transported from one end of the earth to another. The spirit of the chase, of the wild hunt through the waves and the violent battle before the prize was won, was shown in the faces of the crew, set for a fight the moment the ship cast her moorings, although it might be some months before the first whale was sighted. The determined jaw of Captain Pease, master of the ship, as he briefed the officers on the course they would follow, accentuated the same grim expression; it was the captain, indeed who set the mood: the whale was an object of prey and they were after it. The owners of whaling ships expected them to return with the oil barrels fully loaded and this was the tremendous job ahead.

The *Acushnet* itself was a source of wonder and interest to the young mariner. Fresh from the shipyards, with two decks, three masts and a square stern, she measured nearly 105 feet in length, 27 feet in width and 13 feet in depth; some 2800 barrels of sperm and whale oil could be stored in her hold; and amidships, like a pair of huge, cavernous black mouths, stood the tryworks—two enormous iron pots, set in a framework of brick like a chimney, with a furnace chamber and a space underneath for water, to protect the wooden deck. As soon as they brought in the first whale, the tryworks would belch smoke and spit forth grease like some dark monster with twin mouths; but now it stood, black and waiting in the winter blasts, while Herman Melville stared at its outlines and tried to picture the way it was going to look in action.

On the third day out, when he was standing before it during a quiet interval of the late watch, he heard a voice beside him say, "I heard below deck last night that we may be firing up before long."

Herman turned around. The voice belonged to a young sailor, Richard Tobias Greene, known as "Toby," who, like Herman Melville, had been to sea but never before as a whaler. Both had been signed as "ordinary" instead of able seamen, since they had had little experience and knew practically nothing of whaling.

"What do you mean?" Herman asked sharply. He knew they wouldn't sight any whales for some time, till they reached the territory around the Tropic of Cancer.

Toby grinned, his small white teeth shining in the dark. He was a slight fellow, about Herman's age, with black curly hair that clustered outside his woolen sailor's cap, and black gleaming eyes that seemed to be brimming with life. He was quick, deft and had already shown that he could be fiery-tongued if one of the old-timers tried to lord it over the new hands. "Manuel and Juan were telling me that Captain Pease wants to have us greenhorns all trained by the time we reach the Tropic of Cancer." He had a dry, sarcastic humor, a droll way of saying "greenhorns" that made Herman smile.

"How will he do it?" he asked, peering into the face next to him in the dark. He had an idea he was going to like this Toby.

"The Portugees say if we sight so much as a school of porpoises, Captain Pease will give orders to 'lower away.' He wants to fill his barrels with oil in record time and head back for Nantucket. They say he is not a strong man."

Herman remembered then that the captain had not only looked stern, but pale and slightly ill the day he came on board with Gansevoort to sign up. "My brother thought he had stomach trouble." He smiled.

"The Portugees say it's bad luck to sail with a sick captain," Toby offered next. "They say a sick captain is like a broken wheel. Neither one can steer the ship straight on her course."

"They're superstitious, like most sailors—Portugees,

Negro, Indian or Yankee." Herman tapped off on his fingers the different types among the crew. They were indeed an odd lot, from Manuel and Juan besides two other "Portugees," to a full-blooded Indian harpooner, to Nantucketers and discontented New Yorkers, like Toby and himself. If they had not been joined together by the wild venture of a whaling voyage, they would be as far apart as the ends of the earth to which they were sailing. In general, however, the men seemed to be superior to the crew on the *St. Lawrence;* and so far no tyrant like Jackson ruled the forecastle.

Toby moved closer, pulling the collar of his pea jacket up around his ears. The rigging was stiff with ice and the sky above was frosty-bright with cold winter stars. Although the *Acushnet* had set out on a straight southerly course, it would be many days before they left the December blasts behind. When the bleak watch finally ended, they went below to the crowded forecastle which gave no more space to the crew than the *St. Lawrence,* although the *Acushnet* was supposed to be the latest improvement in whalers. If possible, the bunks here were packed more closely together and the air was stuffier. Herman thought to himself as he and Toby pulled off their jackets that if he ever built a ship, he would design comfortable quarters for the crew. It would not make the men lazy, as the officers claimed, but ready and fit for the strenuous work they had to do.

Just how strenuous the job of a whaleman was, he could not know until they sighted the first silver spout, shooting up into the air like a misty fountain, gushing from underseas.

It was about six weeks after they had left port at Fairhaven. They were near Central America in latitude, though far out in the Atlantic, leagues away from any dot of land. For at least a week now the weather had been warm, and Captain Pease gave the usual order to place a lookout at the masthead at all times. Two weeks earlier they had run into a school of porpoises, or bottle-nosed dolphin, as some of the sailors called them, that were speared from the ship. The tryworks were uncovered and fired, the fat fish cut up and rendered like lard in the big cauldrons, as Toby had predicted.

"Not much different from hog-killing time at home," he remarked to Herman out of the corner of his mouth. They stood in a circle with the other sailors, feeding the trypots.

Herman laughed. "Except that this smells much worse." He made a face, remembering the more agreeable odor of pork on his uncle's farm at Broadhall during hog-killing time. Here, besides the strong fishy smell, the fire, fed with cracklings, gave off a greasy black smoke that filled their nostrils. It was disagreeable work, but it had given the new men experience in splicing and peeling blubber, and it had filled a number of barrels with oil that could be mixed with whale oil and sold at the same price.

Now they were waiting, watching and waiting, for the real game. For several days there had been a feeling of suspense about the ship while all was made ready for the first lowering—harpoons and lances sharpened, the lines (Manila rope, coiled in three-foot tubs) brought out and checked, the whaleboats uncovered and strengthened. On this particular afternoon, however, it was so sultry that the men were drowsy with the still heat. Some of them lounged dreamily about the decks or gazed absently over the side at the gray water that reflected a cloud-filled sky.

Herman and Toby had been set to weaving a sword mat by Hall, the second mate and headsman of their boat, for use as additional lashing. All was calm and quiet, save for the gently rolling motion of the ship, which, with the rhythmical passing to and fro of the marline he and Toby were weaving with, made Herman so dreamy that he forgot all about the lookouts posted high above—forgot, in fact, that he was aboard a whaling ship.

Then all at once he "started at a sound so strange, long drawn, and musically wild and unearthly" that the ball of marline dropped from his hand.

"Blo-o-o-o-w!" came the sound again.

Gazing up, he saw the Indian harpooner, "high aloft in the cross-trees. His body was reaching forward, his hand stretched out like a wand, and at brief intervals he continued his cries."

"There she blows! there! there! there! she blows! she blows!"

Toby had picked up the ball of marline, but Herman still stood gazing up at the topmast, rooted to the deck by the chilling cry. The moment had come. A brief look passed between him and Toby but neither spoke. Then came the answering cry of the chief mate.

"Where away?"

"On the lee beam, about two miles off! A school of them!"

The whole ship was thrown into a frenzy of action a moment later when the lookout cried: "There go flukes!" as the whales disappeared with a show of their mighty tail lobes. For within a certain number of minutes they would rise again in another direction, and the crew had to be on the spot, poised and ready for the capture.

"Quick, steward!" cried Captain Pease. "Time, time!"

The steward hurried below, glanced at the watch and reported the exact minute. Then orders were rapped out and the men flew into action like soldiers getting ready to go into battle. Herman, his heart pounding like a drum in his side, heard his name called as oarsman, along with Toby and two others, in the second mate's boat: "Luis, Greene (Toby), Melville!" He was to be a part of the first lowering!

Several of the men were selected as shipkeepers—those not appointed to boats—and one of these relieved the Indian at the mainmast head. (No harpooner was ever made shipkeeper; skilled lance-throwers were too rare.) The sailors at the fore and mizzen came down; the line tubs were fixed in their places in the whaleboats; the davits were thrust out, the mainyard was backed and the three boats swung over the sea "like three samphire baskets over high cliffs." With the rest of the crew, Herman leaped over the bulwarks and "with one hand clung to the rail, while one foot was expectantly poised against the gunwale." He hardly knew what he was doing, his brain was in such a whirl of excitement.

"All ready there?" called out Captain Pease. His pale skin was taut and white with intensity, his eyes hard and narrowed as he scanned the sea watching for some sign of the whales.

"Ready," called back the mates in one breath.

"Lower away then; d'ye hear?" shouted the captain. "Lower away, there!"

"The men sprang over the rail; the sheaves whirled round in their blocks; with a wallow, the three boats dropped into the sea; while, with a dextrous, off-handed daring, unknown in any other vocation, the sailors, goat-like, leaped down the rolling ship's side into the tossed boats below." Herman had no time to think about being a "greenhorn"—he acted as one with the other sailors, swept along by the fury of the chase. He took his place at the second oar, right behind the harpooner-oar, manned by the Indian, and Toby was across from him. Then the men began to bend their backs in rhythm as Hall, who was steersman as well as headsman or whale-killer, began to urge them on with a kind of chant.

"Pull, pull, my fine hearts-alive," he sang. "Pull, my children, pull, my little ones—why don't you break your backbones, my boys? Three cheers, men, all hearts alive! Easy, easy; don't be in a hurry. . . ."

Herman, like the others, pulled with all his strength, but it was not hard enough to suit the second mate.

"Why don't you snap your oars, you rascals? Give way there, give way! The devil fetch ye, ye ragamuffin rapscallions, ye are all asleep! Pull, will ye? Pull, can't ye? Pull, won't ye?" So he coaxed them and badgered them and goaded them into racing the whale boat across the rolling waves to meet the sea monsters, his words growing more and more heated, but his voice was quiet. "Pull, and break something! Pull, and start your eyes out!" He whipped out his knife from his girdle. "Here: every mother's son of ye draw his knife, and pull with the blade between your teeth."

The sailors, panting for breath, reached for their jack-knives, and stuck the blade between their jaws. Herman's pulses were pounding like hammers, his arm muscles were knotted already with the oaring, but somehow biting down on the hard metal helped you to pull harder.

"That's it—that's it!" the mate cried. "Now ye do something; that looks like it, my steel-bits." So he went on, encouraging them and lashing them with the same keen phrases, a mixture of fun and fierceness, yet his tone was always firm.

In much the same way Raymond, the first mate, and Captain Pease were urging on the crews of their boats, though the first mate spoke in an intense whisper and used only a few words: "Strong, strong, my boys! Seethe, seethe her, my lads! Pull, pull, my boys." And Captain Pease commanded his crew more than he cajoled them. His voice was crisp, his orders stern, delivered without the feeling of the mates. All at once he raised his arm, pointed toward a troubled bit of greenish-white water with thin scattered puffs of vapor rising over it—to Herman that was all it seemed, but it meant that just beneath the surface of the bubbling water the whales were swimming! The Indian harpooner who had been standing up in their boat gave voice to the captain's signal the same instant: "Down, down all, and give way—there they are!" and he dropped "like light" to his seat. Then all the boats set off in pursuit of that troubled bit of water, but it flew on and on while the men pulled at their oars until their backs broke and the thin sun that had filtered through the clouds began to set in the late afternoon.

Still the boats tore on. Herman Melville had never in his life come close to a scene like this, even in his dreams. As he wrote long afterward: "It was a sight full of quick wonder and awe! The vast swells of the omnipotent sea; the surging, hollow roar they made as they rolled along the eight gunwales, like gigantic bowls in a boundless bowling green; the brief suspended agony of the boat, as it would tip for an instant on the knifelike edge of the sharper waves, that almost seemed threatening to cut it in two; the sudden profound dip into the watery glens and hollows; the keen spurrings and goadings to gain the top of the opposite hill; the headlong, sledlike slide down its other side—all these, with the cries of the headsmen and harpooners and the shuddering gasps of the oarsmen, with the wondrous sight of the ship bearing down upon her boats with outstretched sails, like a wild hen after her screaming brood—all this was thrilling." No one on earth, he thought, not even a spirit entering the other world, could feel "stranger and stronger emotions than that man does, who for the first time finds himself pulling into the charmed, churned circle of the hunted sperm whale."

By now they could see the jets of vapor shooting forth everywhere to the right and left of the three boats. But the sky was growing darker and the wind was rising. A squall was coming upon them just at this moment! The mist became so thick they could not see the other boats, yet there was no thought of giving up the chase.

"There is time to kill a fish yet before the squall comes —There's white water again! Spring!" The mate Hall whispered to his crew. And a moment later, "Stand up!" to the Indian, who sprang to his feet, harpoon in hand. They still could not see the whales, but they suddenly heard "an enormous wallowing sound, as of fifty elephants, stirring in their litter."

"That's his hump. *There, there,* give it to him!" Hall whispered.

It was maddening not to be able to see; Herman strained forward, but he only heard a short, rushing sound as the darted iron leaped out of the boat. Then, before he knew what was happening, as a gush of scalding vapor from the whale shot up near him, the squall broke loose; the boat seemed to strike on a ledge and something beneath them rolled and tumbled like an earth-

quake. The next instant he and Toby and all of them were tossed "helter-skelter into the white, curdling cream of the squall!" Half-suffocated, gasping for breath in the churning water, it took him a minute to realize where he was. Squall, whale and harpoon all blended together as the crew thrashed in the waves. The whale, merely grazed by the iron, escaped.

After a few moments, they could see that the boat, though swamped with water, was nearly unharmed. Swimming around it, they picked up the floating oars and, lashing them across the gunwale, tumbled back to their places. There they sat up to their knees in the sea, while the storm howled around them. Hours later, the *Acushnet* picked them up, nearly crushing them as it glided close in the misty sea. (The other two boats had cut loose from their fish before the squall, and returned safely to the ship.)

Escaped—the whale had escaped, and the men had nearly lost their lives! Herman, still shaking the water from his jacket, wondered at the risk whalemen took. "Mr. Hall," he asked the mate, "does this sort of thing often happen?"

"Certain," was the answer. "I've lowered for whales from a leaking ship in a gale off Cape Horn."

It was the attitude of all the old-timers; whalemen accepted danger as they accepted the varying moods of the sea, with the same offhand, careless courage. And after all the struggle, they had lost their prize. Herman wondered how they could be so calm about the loss.

However, they were in whaling waters and the lookouts might be expected to give the familiar cry at any time.

A few days later, he and Toby were posted as lookouts,

Toby at the mizzen, he at the "foremost head," his head and shoulders leaning against the slackened royal shrouds. The weather was still sultry, and today the sun shone over a calm, noiseless sea; no porpoises, flying fish or other sea-beings broke the quiet of the gentle waves. High on his perch, Herman found himself swaying to and fro in the enchanted air above the blue water, found his head nodding sleepily, and then his eyes closed. Behind him the other lookouts were dozing, and on deck below the crew, even the helmsman, could not resist a spell of sleep. The *Acushnet* was gliding through the ocean as if in a trance, and young mariner Melville was part of it.

Then suddenly bubbles seemed to burst under his closed eyes, his hands grasped the shrouds instinctively as he came back to life with a shock: there, not forty fathoms off, a gigantic sperm whale lay rolling in the water! Lazily moving up and down, "tranquilly spouting his vapory jet, the whale looked like a portly burgher smoking his pipe of a warm afternoon." Herman's hands gripped the shrouds like vices.

"Blo-o-o-w!" came from his lungs, as long and drawn out as he could make it. At almost the same instant he heard Toby and the other lookout sound the alert and then, as if the sleepy ship awoke all at once, a dozen voices from all parts of the vessel echoed the cry.

"Clear away the boats! Luff!" shouted Captain Pease, and the sailors leaped into action, calling their orders from one to another in fierce, joyous tones of triumph. A huge sperm whale, only forty fathoms off in a calm sea! Their shouts must have alarmed the whale, for he turned and swam majestically away. Herman, watching him intently across the sun-bright sea, hated to destroy his calm afternoon recreation, but a whaling lookout could have no sentimental ideas. Following the huge form with his eyes, he waited until he saw the tail tip upward, the great lobes emerge.

"There go flukes!" he gave the warning, and slid down the rigging to the deck. He and Toby were assigned to Hall's boat as oarsmen, in the same seats they had during the first lowering. When the whale rose again, their boat was much nearer to it than either of the others, which meant that they—or the second mate, as headsman— would have the honor of the capture.

"Start her, start her, my men!" he urged them, his voice quietly intense. "Don't hurry yourselves; take plenty of time—but start her. Start her all; but keep cool, keep cool—easy, easy. Start her!"

"Wa-hee!" screamed the Indian, uttering an old war whoop as they drew closer and closer to the whale, now blowing "mad yeast" from its jet. The men, spurred on by his cries, tugged and strained at their oars. Herman could feel the muscles in his back growing taut, and the sweat ran down his face in streams. Out of the corner of his eye he glanced at Toby. His face was glistening, too; his black curls clung damply to his forehead. He smiled briefly, crookedly at Herman, intent on pulling his oar. At that moment they heard the welcome cry from Hall to the Indian: "Give it to him!"

The harpoon was hurled and "something went hot and hissing along every one of their wrists. It was the magical line." It went whizzing down the center of the boat as the whale, pierced by the harpoon which was attached to the line, tore through the water trying to break away. So fast was the motion of the line that it began to smoke and the mate shouted: "Wet the line, wet the line!"

Herman took off the old tarpaulin hat he had worn all

during his *St. Lawrence* voyage and dashed sea water into it, sloshing the briny foam over the line. Others followed his example. The line began holding its place. The boat flew through the boiling water like a shark all fins. Now Hall and the harpooner had to change places in the boat, a "staggering business truly in that rocking commotion." The men clung with might and main to their seats, balancing themselves and the boat, while the racing whale made the vibrating line as taut as a harpstring and shook both the craft and its crew to the vitals. But hold they must, and did, until at last "the whale slackened his flight."

"Haul in—haul in!" cried the mate. Facing around toward the whale, all hands began pulling the boat up to him. As soon as they were close to his flank, Hall braced his knee against a cleat in the bow for support and stabbed dart after dart into the flying fish. After each throw, the boat had to stern out of the way of the whale's horrible wallow, which might upset them any second, and then range up for another fling. At each thrust of the lance the whale bled; and it was as if they had punctured a living dyke. Again and again the dart went into that writhing wall.

"The red tide now poured from all sides of the monster like brooks down a hill. His tormented body rolled not in brine but in blood, which bubbled and seethed for furlongs behind in their wake. The slanting sun, playing upon the crimson pond in the sea, sent back its reflection into every face, so that they all glowed to each other like red men. And all the while, jet after jet of white smoke was agonizingly shot from the spiracle of the whale. . . ."

"Pull up—pull up!" cried the mate to the bowsman.

"Close to!" The boat ranged close to the fish's flank. Hall, reaching far out over the bow, slowly churned his long lance into the fish and kept it there, carefully churning and churning. He was seeking to find the heart, which all at once was struck. The whale started from his trance into that "unspeakable thing called his flurry." The monster horribly wallowed in his blood, wrapped himself in mad, boiling spray, so that the boat could hardly struggle out into the clear air of day. His spout-hole opened and closed with sharp, cracking breaths. His heart had burst! After another long shudder and a gush of "clotted red gore," he rolled over and lay motionless, a vast corpse in the sea.

Herman thought for a moment that he was going to collapse from exhaustion and release of tension now that it was all over; but there was no time to think or relax. The other boats joined them and all hands of all the crews united in towing the enormous carcass to the ship. The sun had just begun to set when the whale was killed, and it was long after dark before they finally reached the *Acushnet* sending out her two beacon lanterns across the calm sea. So immense was the size of the whale that it could only be budged little by little; it was nearly midnight by the time they drew alongside and Captain Pease gave orders to moor the whale for the night. Chains were thrust clanking through the portholes, and the whale tied by the head to the stern, and by the tail to the bows of the ship. The prize was as long and nearly as broad as the *Acushnet!* Side by side, yoked together in the darkness, ship and whale seemed like two "colossal bullocks."

Herman and Toby stood marveling at the size of the capture before they went below deck to sleep. Both of them had heard and read stories of whales (before Her-

man left New York, he had read the incredible account of
one Mocha Dick, a white whale who had stove and sunk
the ship, *Essex,* within ten minutes; Owen Chase, the first
mate, had published the story in *Knickerbocker Magazine*) ; but it was one thing to learn of legends or yarns
and quite another to grapple with a great monster like
this yourself—or, rather, to be a member of the crew
that captured it.

Toby nudged him. "The first whale of the voyage—
and you sighted it."

"So did you," Herman said.

Toby shook his head. "I was dozing," he confessed.
"I wouldn't have seen it if you hadn't sounded the warning."

A slow smile spread over Herman's face. "I was sound
asleep up there," he confided. "I'll never know what
wakened me—it was like a sixth sense. I saw the bubbles
of the spout through my eyelids, came to and there it
was. But don't tell Hall or Captain Pease."

The two grinned at each other and went arm in arm
down into the forecastle. Though both were so tired,
they slept fitfully in the hot crowded quarters, now and
again waking to the sound of the sharks slashing away at
the huge feast they found suspended at the side of the
ship.

The next night the *Acushnet* "was turned into what
seemed a shamble; every sailor a butcher." First the
enormous cutting tackles, including a cluster of blocks
and a great blubber hook, weighing 100 pounds, were
attached to the whale. Then the entire crew, striking up
a wild chorus, began to work the windlass, turning the
bars with mighty heaves to hoist the carcass of the whale.

The ship careened over on her side, toppling from the

strain; as the windlass turned, rolling the whale over and over, the cutting spades of the mates were slicing through the blubber or skin of the whale as if it were the rind of an orange and they were cutting lines in it before peeling it off. At last, a "swift, startling snap" was heard, with a great swash the ship rolled upward and backward from the whale, and the tackle rose up in sight carrying the first strip of blubber. To Herman's amazement it was raised high in the rigging before it was cut off and then lowered down the hatchway to the blubber room, where it was coiled away, later to be sliced in thin layers for the trypots.

"Look out below!" called a voice from the maintop as the dripping blubber swayed to and fro before it went down the hatchway. Herman, Toby and the two "Portugees" dodged just in time—if the great strip had hit one of them it could have sent him headlong overboard.

"Blubber blanket is like a lead feather bed," said Luis, as they all stood within a safe distance watching the strip slipping through the hatchway hole like an immense serpent.

It was true. The "blanket" of the whale was soft, but so heavy with fat from which tons of oil would come that it was hazardous to stand near one swinging piece! Now the tackle was lowered again, the windlass turned, and the second strip was cut. As they toiled and sang and sweated over this "leviathan" of the sea, it seemed to the young mariner that they were all pygmies at work on a giant butchering job and that some day one of these giants would seek revenge on all whaling vessels. It was said that the famous Mocha Dick had sunk the *Essex* deliberately after the harpooning of three whales in his shoal. Perhaps whales, like elephants, and they were elephants of the sea, did not forget.

The stripping went on. The head of the whale was cut off and hoisted against the ship's side, where it hung in iron cables, so the pure liquid oil could be bailed out of its hollow "case" by the sailors when the stripping was finished. That job was completed only after long hours of labor and then Captain Pease gave the order, "Haul in the chains! Let the carcass go astern!" and "the peeled, white body of the whale, still colossal," was set adrift in the sea, surrounded by sharks and screaming fowls that flew down from the sky to get their share of the feast.

Herman watched the headless phantom float farther and farther away from the *Acushnet,* wondering, as the white mass became dimmer and dimmer, whether the ghosts of whales returned to haunt the ships of their captors. He shivered a little though the tropical night was warm, and soon picked his way across the littered deck toward the hatchway to join the other sailors who had already gone below.

The next morning, before they had a chance to start the tryworks, a large Right whale was sighted by Juan, the boats were lowered and a new chase begun. Herman, his arms still aching from the first one, thought his muscles were going to burst through his skin as he pulled, pulled, pulled on the oars again. This time it was Raymond, the first mate, who had the "honor of capture," so that Herman and Toby, in Hall's boat, had a chance to witness the harpooning, darting and all the rest of it without being so much a part of it that they could hardly tell what was happening. When the Right whale was dead, they all joined in towing it to the ship as they had the sperm whale, and before the night was over, it had been stripped and beheaded. Now the *Acushnet* sailed on, flanked by a whale-head on either side, a full-burdened ship, making a good start at collecting her 2800 barrels of oil.

The Right whale was aged and diseased and, strangely enough, from the great sore on one of its flanks, the mate dug down and brought up a "purse" of ambergris, a soft yellow wax that smelled like "spring violets." Perfumes and pomades were made of ambergris, colognes and fragrant candles. It had formed into globules floating around in the liquid part and Herman, along with Toby, Juan and Manuel, were set to squeezing the lumps back into liquid. The four sat cross-legged on the deck around a great tub of the sweet-smelling wax, squeezing and squeezing the soft, fragrant substance, under a blue sky, with the sun shining on their backs and the sea calm beneath the ship. After the excitement of the second chase and the "bitter exertion at the windlass" again, it was a healing task—to crush the soft yellow lumps in your hand and inhale the perfume as they broke. How good the wax felt to the calluses made by the oars, the lines and the windlass bars. All morning long the four sailors sat, scarcely saying a word, only pressing the lumps between their fingers until their hands were like eels, sliding around in the tub.

Herman felt a deep contentment steal over him. He thought of his friend, Fly, whom he had left poring over notebooks at a desk in New York; but for his poor handwriting he, Herman Melville, might be doing the same thing. The life of a whaleman was dangerous, rough and hard hitting, but it was stimulating, exotic, even poetic in a wild, brutal way. Not for anything in the world would he want to exchange places with his friend at the copying desk, or with Gansevoort, studying law books all day long. And schoolteaching seemed drudgery indeed!

That night the tryworks were fired up for the rendering of blubber from both whales. The great pots were kept clean and polished when not in use till the inside shone "like silver punchbowls." Now Hall gave the word to the cook to "off hatch" and "fire the works." It was an easy job to start the blaze, since the ship's carpenter had been shoving his savings in the furnaces all during the voyage. And once the first batch of blubber had been rendered, the flames could be fed with the scraps or "fritters," just as they had with the porpoises.

Soon the pots were boiling and bubbling with whale oil, which was not disagreeable in the same way as the other fish had been, but had "an unspeakable, wild, Hindoo odor about it," like "a funeral pyre." By midnight the works were in full operation. The fierce flames leaped out of the sooty flues, lighting up every rope in the rigging, making the sails look like broad sheets of fire. The harpooners, "always the whale-ship's stokers, pitched hissing masses of blubber into the scalding pots with huge pronged poles. The smoke rolled away in sullen heaps." It was impossible not to breathe the black clouds into your lungs.

The windlass, opposite the mouth of the works, served as a "sea-sofa" for members of the watch when not otherwise occupied. They lounged against its side, "looking into the red heat of the fire till their eyes felt scorched in their heads." Herman stood with the others, staring into the flames, fascinated by the barbaric sight of the harpooners, feeding the fat and the fire; by the faces of the men, "all begrimed with smoke and sweat," and by the ship itself, like a burning vessel on the broad black sea.

Some of the sailors tossed hard sea biscuit into the boiling grease. This, one of them informed Herman, made a delicacy out of the usual hard, tasteless biscuit. "You ought to try one," he advised; and before the night was over, both Herman and Toby had dipped their biscuit in whale oil and found it a tasty snack.

While they watched, the sailors began to tell stories of their adventures, "tales of terror told in words of mirth." Presently, as always, the talk turned to the legend of Mocha Dick, the white-humped whale, and the men began to speculate as to whether he really sank the *Essex* or not. Hall, who was standing near by, joined in the discussion.

"I've twice sailed under Owen Chase," he said, "and I always knew him to speak the truth."

Herman felt suddenly that he must find out more about the man who wrote that strange narrative. "Tell me, Mr. Hall," he spoke out eagerly in spite of his shyness with officers. "Did you really know the remarkable Owen Chase?"

"Aye," the second mate nodded, his beard reflecting the glow of the red-hot tryworks. He was an Englishman who had served many years in the American whaling industry.

"What was he like?" Herman pressed him. "He must have been a strong man to be the only survivor of the wreck."

"Aye, he was—and he was fair to the men. A hard man but a just one, as whalers go."

"What did he look like?" Herman pursued.

Hall shrugged his shoulders. "Like lots of whaling

officers. A flinty face, steely blue eyes; strong, straight mouth as I remember. Once, when we were rounding Cape Horn. . . ." and he was off on a tale of Owen Chase's mastery of the ship during a severe blow.

"They say Owen Chase has sworn to capture Mocha Dick," one of the men put in. "He wants revenge for the whale's revenge."

Revenge for revenge. What could make a man regard a whale as a personality, a force to be reckoned with? Yet all whales were. They made it felt in the ferocious and often cunning fight they put up. And why shouldn't they want revenge on their hunters? As Herman looked around at the sailors, they seemed like feverish devils working in front of the red-hot inferno of the tryworks. Whaling was a strange business, compounded of struggle and strain and the triumph over tremendous odds; yet it was after all an industry in which men worked to supply a commodity to the "civilized" world of 1841, that lit up the darkness of its homes with whale oil lamps. Why then should a man pursue a single whale across endless seas, hoping to capture that one and only that one whale? Herman wished he could see Owen Chase and judge for himself what sort of man he was. He wished he had had a copy of the narrative in *Knickerbocker Magazine,* so he could read it over again.

The second wish was granted unexpectedly one day a few weeks later, when the *Acushnet* "spoke" the whaler *Lima* south of the equator. (They had in the meantime put in at Rio de Janeiro on the thirteenth of March, with 150 barrels of oil, which they sent home by the brig, *Tweed,* which was heading north. Herman had wanted to visit the city on "the bay of all beauties," backed by the famous Sugar Loaf mountain, but Captain

Pease would not allow any of the sailors shore leave. They stayed two days in port and the only glimpse Herman got of Rio came when he and Toby were part of the ship's crew rowing Captain Pease to the docks to purchase fresh supplies. It had been a great disappointment to both young sailors not to be granted a single day's leave in one of the most important cities of the southern hemisphere.) When two ships met—"spoke"—each other at sea, they usually held what was called a "gam," an exchange of visits by boats' crews—a kind of whalers' gabfest, generally on cruising ground. The two captains would remain on one ship, and the two chief mates on the other. The crews usually gathered in the forecastle to exchange sea gossip. The *Lima* was a Nantucket craft fairly loaded with oil, from the answer her captain gave to the first hail: "How many barrels?" with which whalers always greeted each other.

Captain Pease did not seem too well pleased to hear that the *Lima* had been more successful than the *Acushnet,* but he had to be civil and accept the invitation to "gam" with her a couple of days. Herman was among the crew that rowed him across to the other ship; when they were all on board, the two captains retired to the cabin and the two crews lounged in the forecastle seated in twos and threes on the rough bunks, talking their sailors' lingo. It was not long before the conversation turned to the latest news of the white-humped whale, Mocha Dick.

"Our second mate, Mr. Hall, sailed with Owen Chase for two three-year voyages," Herman told the others, a touch of pride in his voice. "He doesn't seem to know any more about the *Essex* story than anybody else, but he says Chase always spoke the truth."

"Here's one who ought to know," said one of the

Lima crew, putting his hand on the shoulder of a young sailor, not more than sixteen, sitting beside him. "He's Owen Chase's son, William Henry!" He clapped him on the back. "Speak up, Willie!"

The boy grinned good-naturedly. Herman had noticed earlier that he was a fine-looking lad, different from the usual run of sailors.

"What would you like to know about the *Essex?*" he asked Herman, crossing over to sit beside him.

He was a frank and friendly boy, and Herman questioned him about the story—whether the ship had really been sunk by the whale, whether there were no other survivors, just how the whale had rammed the ship—all the questions he had wondered about when he thought over the strange story during the lonely night watches in the foremast. Before they finished talking, the order came from above for the crew of the *Acushnet* to return to their ship. However, they came back the next morning; and as soon as the boy saw Herman, he went to his chest and brought out a complete copy of the narrative his father had written, which he handed to the young mariner who had shown so much interest.

"This is my own copy," he said. "I thought you might like to look at it."

Herman thanked him and that night, on the landless sea, close to the very latitude of the shipwreck itself, he read the wondrous story. It had a surprising effect on him. He felt as if he had had that experience himself, as if he had been the sole survivor of the catastrophe. The next day, before the two whalers ended the gam and sailed their separate ways, he returned the narrative to the author's son and thanked him again.

Many times during the days and nights that followed,

when there was a lull in the constant chase, the sweat and strain of the cutting and rendering of blubber, Herman Melville pondered over the story of the *Essex* and its fatal battle with Mocha Dick. For several weeks there was no letup in the work; the sailors went to their bunks so exhausted they felt as if the marrow had been sucked from their bones, and were roused a few hours later to start in on another chase. Sometimes, before they could clean the decks of the smoke and grease from one rendering, another was begun; or again, when they had just cleared the debris, and all was spotlessly clean, it was immediately messed up once more. Yet there were short periods when no whales were sighted, or when they spoke a ship and gammed with her, perhaps to learn more news of the deeds of Mocha Dick, that gave Herman a chance to mull over the extraordinary tales, trying to discover the meaning that lay behind the struggles between man and the monsters of the sea.

The *Acushnet* continued its course down the eastern coast of South America toward Cape Horn, and the weather grew cold and the winds blew and the men froze their beards during a single watch. (One of the sailors, nicknamed Jack "Nastyface" because his skin was rough as a macadamized road, looked as if his cheeks had been rutted by cart wheels in the biting cold.) They passed Staten Land in April and saw it gleaming "like a pile of glaciers in Switzerland." They rounded the cape in a squall and beat their way through heavy gales. Herman saw his first albatross when he came up to the "overclouded deck" from the forenoon watch below on the nineteenth of April—a "regal, feathery thing of unspotted whiteness, with a hooked, Roman bill." The fierce blow had dashed it against the main hatches.

They were in the teeth of the gale for three days, facing constant danger, but Captain Pease was able to steer the ship on its northward way toward sunshine once more. By the first week in May they were chasing sperm whales west of Valparaiso. Herman and Toby were both becoming experienced hands at whaling now. They knew the signs of troubled air above the water, the time of a whale's soundings and the moment he went into his "flurry." They could handle their oars and keep out of the whizzing line's burn; they could work far into the night splicing and peeling blubber and standing before the try-works as well as any of the old-timers on board. And they were becoming fast friends.

By the time the ship reached Callao and the harbor of Santa, where they stopped for ten days, the two young sailors took in all the sights they could in the little time Captain Pease allowed the men ashore. One of the crew, David Smith, vowed he had had enough of whaling and deserted two days before they got under way. But Herman was quite well contented. He wrote Gansevoort that he was in perfect health and fortunate in being a member of a crew superior to most whaling crews, though he was thinking mostly of Toby. Moreover, he was at last in the blue Pacific, seeing some of the ports that his cousin Thomas had talked about; he was leading a life of adventure.

And one day, the *Acushnet* spoke a ship, the *Charles-Carroll,* whose captain proved to be Owen Chase himself! Herman, being a mere foremast hand, had no chance to talk to him, but the young mariner considered it a stroke of great good fortune that it had come to pass that he finally saw the author of the famous narrative in person. Chase came on board for two hours at a time, and

Herman managed to stand close enough while the two captains conversed on the quarter-deck, to study the remarkable man who had survived the shipwreck. He was a large, powerful well-made man; rather tall; to all appearances something past forty-five or so; with a handsome face for a Yankee and expressive of great uprightness and calm, quiet courage. It was a face that Herman Melville never forgot, and one he would make immortal when the time came.

8

JUMPING SHIP

THE *Acushnet* sailed on and on, searching for whale. Captain Pease grew more surly and grim as the months went by and the bulk of the barrels remained empty. The luck that had filled at least a third of the casks during the first part of the voyage turned bad as soon as they left Callao, but the master would not give up, would not return to New Bedford nor even put in for fresh supplies at some port along the route from one whaling ground to another.

Herman Melville began to feel that the thrill and excitement of capturing whales was not enough to make up for the day-to-day monotony, the miserable life of the forecastle during the months when there was no chase. Even the mystery and wonder of the sea itself could not compensate for the roughness and brutality of a whaler's lot. Food supplies dwindled to the bare necessities of salt beef and hard sea biscuit, meal after meal, until you could hardly stomach it. When one of the sailors complained to Captain Pease about the meager fare, the only reply he got was the butt end of a handspike against the seat of his pants, a blow that nearly threw him to the deck.

"Now, get below, you sea dog, and don't bother me again with your measly troubles. I've trouble enough as it is!" And the captain turned away to scan the horizon with his eternal spyglass.

His surliness brought out the meanness in the men, who became irritable and quarrelsome with each other as the days went by and there was nothing but an occasional "gam" with another ship to break the monotony. Jack "Nastyface" lived up to his name in disposition as well as complexion. The first time the ship crossed the equator in the Pacific, he was at the masthead, looking out for whales. When eight bells struck and he slid down for his relief, Herman and Toby were coming up on deck. Hailing him, they told him the ship had just crossed "the line."

"The devil we did," he snarled sarcastically. "Can't ye tell us some news? Didn't I see it as well as you did, and better, too? Wasn't I aloft? I saw the line before any man aboard." He glared at them, the rugged lines of his face filled with sweaty dirt. Then he headed for the hatchway before they could say another word.

The two looked at each other, but saved their sniggers

till they were aloft; even they knew the equator was an imaginary line. "It's a good thing we didn't laugh down there, though," Toby said, settling himself against the masthead. "Old Nastyface's nasty enough as it is!"

"He's not the only one," Herman observed. "Have you noticed that the men don't joke or sing any more? They don't even sing out at a rope!"

"I know," Toby agreed soberly.

"Six men deserted already," Herman counted on his fingers. "Our first mate is gone." (He had had a fight with Captain Pease at Payta, Peru, and had left the ship.) "Three men put ashore, half dead with disease." He shrugged. "But what's the difference to a sea captain with his eye on one thing? Oil, profitable oil!"

"If only we'd sight a whale it wouldn't be so bad," Toby sighed. "At least then there'd be something to do. We'd be risking our necks again."

Herman smiled at his friend. "That's right. A school of sperm whales would be a welcome sight just now. But more than that, I think Captain Pease should put in at the next port for fresh supplies, fresh fruit if possible— before we all die of scurvy—and a fresh sight for men's eyes, the sight of land. I think every sailor should have shore leave—not just a day, but a week or maybe a month—before we go on with our mission to fill the barrels or break our backs in the attempt!" He brought his fist down on the topsail yard where they were resting.

"Fat chance there is of a whaleman getting more than a few hours ashore!" Toby bit morosely into a piece of biscuit he had put into the pocket of his jacket at supper time. "Especially from our dear, kind Captain Pease; he wouldn't give a sailor leave to visit his dying mother if she

happened to be in port. Ptuii!" Toby spit out the bite
of biscuit and threw the rest out over the water. "Rot-
gut!"

They watched the tiny white speck disappear as it
dropped into the dark waves below. It was a gloomy
night; the days and weeks had been gray and gloomy,
hot and humid for some time now. The ship swept through
the Pacific, from one cruising ground to another, but they
seemed always to miss the whales by a few days, sometimes only a few hours, according to the captains of other
ships the *Acushnet* spoke as she plied her course through
the "off-shore ground" westward from Peru and Ecuador.

One day they approached the Galápagos group of islands, better known as the "Encantadas," or Enchanted
Isles, as the Spaniards called them, because from the trade
winds and cross currents near their shores they seemed
ever to be shifting from place to place in the sea. The
light winds and sudden calms, the treacherous currents
that had wrecked many a vessel on the reefs baffled more
than one sea captain into going around and around without headway until he nearly lost his mind before he finally
steered his ship back into the open sea. Yet Captain Pease
took the *Acushnet* into the shunned, deserted area because
he had heard that whales sometimes calved near one of
the islands.

Herman stood at the side with some of the other sailors
as they drew near the twisted, jagged shores. The Enchanted Isles—they looked indeed as if they had been
bewitched, turned to stone made out of the ashes of
some great fire. They were volcanic islands, he knew;
and they appeared to his eyes like nothing so much as
twenty-five mountainous heaps of cinders, dumped in a
vacant lot near the old house on Bleecker Street, the

"vacant lot, the sea." A desolate sight for sailors longing to lay their eyes on good green earth!

No whales were to be found, but the captain thought some tortoises might be captured to furnish a change of diet free of cost. He well knew there was discontent among the men! At noon he sent a boat's crew ashore, "with orders to see all they could, and bring back whatever tortoises they could" carry. Neither Herman nor Toby were among the crew and they waited impatiently all afternoon for the boat to come back. It was after sunset when the dinghy returned weighted down with three huge tortoises. Ropes were dropped over and all hands strained to pull up the strange, "antediluvian-looking" creatures, that seemed to have crawled from beneath the foundations of the world. They were chained to the deck, and when his shipmates had gone below, Herman took a lantern and examined the crusted shells, black and heavy as shields, covered here and there with patches of moss like ancient ruins of walls.

All night long he heard the slow dragging and clumping, the rattle of chains as the tortoises moved clumsily back and forth across the deck. He dreamed he was sitting cross-legged on one of the tortoises in a wild nightmare that lasted till morning. But the next night he sat down to a feast of tortoise steaks and tortoise stews along with the other sailors, and with them helped carve out the shells into three mammoth soup tureens.

A few days later he was among the crew sent out to fish among the waters at the foot of Rock Rodondo, a natural tower rising like a crenelated peak from one of the islands. Formed of shelved layers of clinkers and infested with nests of screaming sea fowls on each shelf, the Rock was so covered with bird lime it looked from the

distance like a white sail suddenly looming up out of nowhere. The three fishing boats rowed up to this strange
tower just at dawn, when Herman had his first closeup
view of the Encantadas. It gave him an eerie feeling—
all was silent and still, except for the yawks and screams
of the birds, pelicans, penguins, hawks—"bandit birds
with long bills cruel as daggers."

The island itself was a maze of blackened thickets,
leafless and dead; the only sign of life was the creepy
movement of a thousand crawling creatures—lizards,
snakes, spiders, tortoises and the strange aguano, a reptile
native to the Encantadas. Herman felt his skin begin to
crawl and Toby's face turned a sickly yellow. Even the
toughest of the seamen, who had visited the Encantadas
many times before, was ready to turn back after an hour
or so.

"A man could lose his mind wanderin' among those
wicked creepin' devils!" he grunted, mopping his brow.
The others were more than ready to follow him, wiping
the sweat from their faces. They were all hot and thirsty.
No mountain streams ran from the hard lava hills of the
Encantadas, no lakes spotted the ashen gray valleys, for
no rain ever fell on the leaden group of islands. Occasionally, on the northern tip of Albermarle, the one
faintly habitable place, the dews fell from green but
fruitless trees, and the few stray wanderers who lived
there from time to time would catch the precious drops
in a calabash or gourd.

Herman, curious about Rock Rodondo and its unusual
formation, suggested that they climb to the top, but Toby
was the only one who was game to try. The others
started fishing.

"Whaddya think this is, a shore leave you're on?" said

Jack Nastyface. "We're supposed to do a day's fishin'!"

"I don't think it will take long to fill the boats with all we can carry, from the looks of the waters here." Herman pointed to the pools among the rocks at the base of the tower, where thousands of "fairy fish" leaped and swam. It was a vast aquarium of tropical fish of every hue and shape imaginable. "Suppose the rest of you try your luck while we try the tower," he suggested. "Then we'll take over when we come down."

"That won't be long, I'll lay ye odds!" predicted another one of the crew. "Ye'll never reach the top."

Herman and Toby paid no attention to him. They started the difficult climb from ledge to ledge, trying to avoid the seafowls' nests, most of which were empty now; the birds had flown away at the first sight of the strangers. Sometimes a hen pecked at their hands as they started to hoist themselves from one shelf of rock to another. Sometimes the shelf was so narrow they could hardly hang on. But they finally reached the top, and from its height could see all twenty-five of the charred, still islands, floating in the blistering sun. It was a peculiar picture, one that Herman was to remember years afterward, when he stood in the Adirondack mountains, struck by the contrast of richness and barrenness in the two parts of the earth.

When they descended, both Toby and he caught their share of fish, for hardly had their hooks touched the water when some finny mouth leaped out to grab the bait. For several days the men had fresh fish to eat, but the welcome change did not last long. Captain Pease decided to move on. They roamed the seas once more, stopping briefly at the *Sandwich Isles,* but no one was allowed ashore.

Then at last, after another weary six months of luckless cruising, except for the capture of one or two Right whales whose yield of oil was poor, word came from the quarter-deck that made the men jump for joy: they were headed for the Marquesas!

The Marquesas—most famed and beautiful of all the islands in the Pacific. The South Sea Islands—lovely houris, native girls dancing in grass skirts; fresh fruits; coconuts and bunches of ripe bananas! It couldn't be true; it was too good to be true! During the days that followed, the men became lazy and mellow as the weather cleared and the goal drew closer and closer. The skies were blue, the sea soft and calm, the waters empty of game, so all the sailors had to do was to stand their regular watches— though most of the time they leaned or lounged through their hours of duty, dreaming of the good times ahead when they reached the Marquesas. The dreary food, the scanty supply of drinking water—which was getting so low it had to be rationed—and the brutal ways of Captain Pease were all overlooked while they enjoyed the pleasant cruise through waters that took them farther and farther from the blistering equator; they dreamed or gossiped about the Marquesas or dozed under the canopy they set up on deck above the forecastle. Even Herman, who liked to read whenever he had any extra time, could not take a book in his hands without falling asleep inside of five minutes. From the time the *Acushnet* entered the waters of the South Seas, the voyage took on the quality of a dream.

They were all due for a rude awakening. When the ship entered the beautiful horseshoe Bay of Nukuhiva the men leaned over the side, lost in admiration of the sight in front of them. It had a sparkling magnificence, a grandeur beyond anything that Herman had expected, in spite of the many times he had heard his cousin Tom praise the beauty of the South Sea Islands. From the shore the land rose gradually on all sides in long green slopes that swelled into "lofty and majestic heights," blue against the sky. Deep glens descended from the mountains and down each valley flowed a rushing stream which became a silver cascade as it fell. Scattered irregularly along beneath the shady branches of coconut trees, the yellow bamboo houses of the natives were golden patches against the many-shaded green and blue background.

The only flaw in the picture, in Herman's eyes, was the flotilla of French warships lying in the harbor. "Four heavy, double-banked frigates and three corvettes to frighten a parcel of naked heathen into subjection!" he thought to himself. (The French had taken possession of the islands several weeks before, scaring the natives into submission with their great military show of cannon, Congreve rockets and soldiers.) But in spite of this he was as eager as the rest of the crew to explore the island. They were all ready to spring ashore the moment the anchor was dropped.

Captain Pease, however, issued orders that there would be no shore leave until all the supply and repair duties were done, and then each watch was to have one day. One day! Only a single day to themselves on land when they had been six long months at sea without putting into port once! It was an outrage. The men grumbled and groaned against their fate, but not one of them (nor even two or three banded together) would protest against the captain's tyranny, because too many of them had seen sailors who did end up by "walking the plank."

The ship was boarded by friendly natives who came bringing coconuts in their canoes, and by young girls who came swimming out to welcome the sailors. (It was taboo for island women to ride in canoes.) Their visits made the men only more anxious to go ashore, but the captain kept them busy repairing the rigging, getting rid of the barnacles that encrusted the prow of the *Acushnet,* patching the sails and the thousand other things that had to be done to a whaling ship when she finally put in after long months at sea.

The rare glimpses the men had of the land came when they rowed the captain ashore for exchange of news with the French admirals or when such supplies as the islands afforded were bought up to be stored in the hold. Herman was part of the crew taking the captain once or twice, and each time he learned all he could about the island. He found out that besides the people of Nukuhiva, who hated but feared the French, there were tribes of savages living in the valleys on the other side of the mountains back of the harbor city. One of these, the Happars, were the ancient enemies of the other, the Typees, who lived in the valley of an intervening mountain. The Typees were "known" cannibals—dreaded by invaders and natives alike. They were known also as such fierce warriors that the French had not dared to enter the interior for fear the one hundred soldiers they had brought on the warships would be wiped out. "Typee" on Nukuhiva meant "Cannibal." Yet the island itself was so alluring that Herman was drawn to it irresistibly. He wanted to discover what life was like in these tribes back of the blue mountains; not the Typees: he would steer clear of them if he had the chance to explore; but he could discover no harm in the ways of the Happars, and there must be several villages of them, scattered throughout their valley. Each time he came back to the meanness and misery of the ship he thought of the waving coconut palms, the beautiful breadfruit trees and the green grasses under the soft skies, all so close at hand, yet denied to the sailors who needed them so much.

The *Acushnet* had been in the harbor only a few days when he made up his mind to run away.

Run away! "Jump ship," as the sailors said. It was a daring scheme, and he thought it over carefully, planning the steps. He could not take the chance of being caught and brought back aboard to be thrown into irons. He would make his getaway up the mountains somehow, and would stay there, living off fruits and coconuts, until the ship sailed. He pictured himself sitting under the swaying fronds of the tree, looking down on the "detested old vessel" and watching her sail away while he lounged in splendid tropical leisure.

He could not sleep; he was too busy planning his escape. And one night he stole up on deck to mull over the best means; he had told nobody his secret, not even Toby. It was very dark on deck and he leaned over the bulwarks, revolving in his mind the various plans that had come to him. He had not been there long when he realized someone was leaning over the side near him, someone also lost in a deep reverie. He recognized the figure even in the dim light.

He moved closer. "Toby?"

"Yes."

"How long have you been here?"

"I don't know. I couldn't stand it down there any more!"

"Nor I." They were quiet a moment. Then Herman continued in whispers: "Toby—were you having the same dream I was?"

"I think so. I've had enough! You too?"

Herman nodded. After another pause while they seemed to read each other's minds, he went on: "Tomorrow? When we're on *leave?*" He spoke the word sarcastically. The starboard watch, to which they both belonged, was to have its day ashore beginning the next morning.

It took only a few words more to complete their plans, and they shook hands on the bargain, each going below separately, noiselessly, in order not to arouse suspicion.

Soon after the decks had been washed down the following day, Captain Pease summoned the starboard watch to the quarter-deck and harangued the men on their leave, warning them against the natives and ordering them to be back at the ship before sunset. "At two bells the boat will be manned to take you off," he finished, "and the Lord have mercy on you!"

He had hardly finished speaking before the men moved in a body toward the forecastle to get ready. Herman and Toby took advantage of the general confusion to prepare for their getaway. They would not load themselves down, but would take a few items to use if they had to buy the good-will of the natives. Herman thrust a pound or two of tobacco and several yards of cotton cloth into his sailor's blouse, and Toby did the same. They put on their stoutest shoes and heavy duck trousers and jackets for the climb up the mountain. When one of their mates commented on their clothes, Toby said quickly, "We're not going to the bottom of our chests for a parcel of heathen! We're saving our best till we get to the Spanish main!" He rolled his eyes, and the men laughed. The two runaways exchanged a look of relief. They couldn't take a chance of letting the others in on the scheme: someone would have been only too ready to turn them in to the captain, in hopes of a paltry reward.

Just as they were ready to leave, Herman lingered in the forecastle, looking around for something else to take, and his eye lit on the bread-barge and beef-kid. Some instinct told him to grab a handful of sea biscuit and shove them into his blouse along with the tobacco and cloth. . . . "Melville!" he heard his name bellowed from above, and up the hatchway he ran.

Before they reached the shore, a tropical rain had started, and by the time they reached the boat, it was pouring. They all fled for shelter under an immense canoe shed near the beach. The rain continued without stopping, its monotonous beating on the shed making the men drowsy, and presently they threw themselves on the large war canoes and fell asleep.

This was the chance Herman and Toby had been waiting for. Without saying a word to each other they crept out of the shed and plunged into a deep grove of trees. After ten minutes they came to an open space and could see the ridge they wanted to climb. But the way lay through a road of native huts, and they dared not run the risk of being seen, so they went roundabout through a growth of thickets. The rain was still falling, and their clothes were getting heavy, but they pushed on. When they finally came to the bottom of the ridge they found the path blocked by a mass of yellow reeds, "stubborn as so many rods of steel." It was impossible to break a passage through them by pushing, but Toby finally tried slashing at them with his jackknife, and with both of them hacking away they came to the foot of the mountain. They still had scarcely spoken.

Now Herman took his companion's arm. "Let's not look back until we stand at the summit," he said in a low tense voice. "Let's shove ahead—then we can laugh. You are the nimblest, so lead on, Toby, and I'll follow."

"All right, brother," Toby said, "quick's our play. Only let's keep close together, that's all." He cleared a brook across their path with one leap and started up the mountain.

They climbed steadily; at times the ascent was difficult and dangerous, but they kept on, not once turning their faces toward the sea. At about three hours before sunset, they found themselves standing on what seemed to be the highest land on the island, more than three thousand feet above sea level. From this height the scenery was magnificent.

The two runaways stood for a moment gazing down at the lonely Bay of Nukuhiva, ringed around on three sides by mountains, whose green slopes led to smiling and fertile valleys. Then Herman Melville and Richard Tobias Greene looked at each other and laughed aloud for joy: they had made their escape!

9

THE MYSTERIOUS VALLEY OF TYPEE

IT WAS TRUE, they had escaped; but now Herman and
Toby had to decide how to go down the other side of
the mountain—which way would lead them to the valley
of the Happars and which one to the dreaded land of the
Typees? Darkness set in soon after they reached the top
of the mountain, and then the rain began to fall again.
They made a flimsy lean-to out of some branches and
huddled under them for shelter, but the downpour lasted
all night long. Herman had slipped on a rocky ledge during the climb, injuring his leg, which began to swell and
ache so during the night that he couldn't sleep. He twisted

and turned, hoping to find a comfortable position for his leg, and at the same time keep out some of the soaking rain. Toward dawn he fell into a painful doze.

He was awakened soon afterward by Toby, who was shaking him by the shoulders. "Melville! To the mast-head, shipmate!" He was in high spirits, refreshed by the night's sleep.

"Huh? O-o-o-h!" Herman groaned sleepily as he moved his leg and the pain shot through like a knife.

He sat up. The rain had stopped, but their clothes were drenched and soggy, clinging damply to their bodies like sheets. The trees were still dripping and the air was heavy with moisture.

"No lookout duty today, my hearty!" Toby went on gleefully. "Except to find the best way down the mountain. But first, I'm starved—did you bring anything to eat?"

"Only a handful of biscuit. You?"

"The same."

They dived into their shirt-fronts, only to discover that the rain had made a doughy mass of the hard bread and tobacco, a messy glob that stuck to their fingers and looked anything but edible, a brackish, mustard-colored goo with slivers of brown tobacco running through it.

"Ugh!" Toby was ready to throw it away, but Herman stayed his arm.

"Give that to me," he said. "I'll mix it with mine. This may be all we'll have to eat for some time. There weren't any fruit trees up here, if you remember."

He was right. They had both been aware in the dying daylight as they made the lean-to that there appeared to be nothing they could eat on the mountain top—no coco-nut trees as Herman had pictured—nor even any berries

or roots; but neither one wanted to alarm the other. Now
they had to face the fact. Somewhat sobered, Toby
handed over his lump of dough. "At least take the tobacco out of it," he said.

"Then there would be nothing left!" Herman put the
two together, but even then it was only enough to make
a couple of mouthfuls for a husky sailor. This, however,
he divided into six pieces with his jackknife, and wrapped
each piece in a strip which he tore from the silk necker-
chief he had put around his throat when they were "dress-
ing up" for shore leave. The little packages would be their
rations for the next two days, he figured; by then they
would be down in the Happar valley.

They crawled cautiously out of the shelter to recon-
noiter. They dared not stand upright for fear of being
spotted from below. By now Captain Pease would have
some lookout on the watch for the two runaways. They
could see the *Acushnet* lying at anchor far below; it was
hard to believe that anyone could spot them. Yet Herman
knew from experience how far the eye of the captain's
spyglass could roam and how clearly two figures stood
out on a rocky cliff. He and Toby crouched low, walking
on all fours. Herman groaned with every step; his leg
was still swelling and the flashes of pain grew worse.

When they looked down over the other side of the
mountain, the prospect was discouraging. There were only
two paths of descent and neither one led directly to the
valleys below, but descended to lower mountain ranges,
and there were deep crevices along the way. At this
height they seemed like cracks in the rock, but they were
probably wide gaps, impossible to cross. The runaways
would have to go around the rims, and it might take days;
they could never survive on six pellets of putrid dough.

And which way led to the valley they were seeking? That was the main question.

Straight down from the summit ran a rushing stream, actually a gorge, falling and swirling among the rocks, although the water was not deep. After much discussion, when they had strained their eyes in every direction and tried several points unsuccessfully, Toby suggested that they should follow the stream—leap down with it from rock to rock. "That's the straightest path," he pointed out. "And I think it leads to Happar Valley."

Herman was not so sure. He was not sure of anything at the moment. His leg throbbed, and a grueling day or longer in the rocky stream wasn't going to help it any. But they couldn't hesitate much more and Toby, once he had made up his own mind, urged Herman to try his plan. "I'll help you along," he offered. "If you have to, you can sit and slide down with the current!" He was in high spirits again, and he imbued Herman with some of his enthusiasm.

"All right, let's go! But first we'd better have breakfast!" Herman handed him one of the tiny packages and unwrapped one for himself. They chewed the morsel slowly, carefully, wanting to get the benefit out of every speck, although the taste of it was enough to make a man sick at any other time. Then they started for the stream.

It was a dangerous and nerve-wracking trek, slow and full of pitfalls they had not reckoned on: the current was increasingly strong; the rocks were jagged, and they could find nothing to hang onto but slippery roots which threatened to give way. Herman was forced to "sit and slide," but even so his leg received further scratches and bruises. By nightfall they were little more than halfway down, their rations were half gone and they were famished.

They crept onto a shelf of overhanging rock, both of them weary from the endless scrambling, jumping and sliding to keep from being dashed to pieces. As if that were not enough, more rain came pelting on the rocks. The boys were wet as it was, but to have to spend another night in the rain seemed too much. This time they crawled under some dead branches that had fallen on the ledge, and huddled together for warmth. Herman was feverish with pain, nearly delirious. Neither one could sleep.

"Remember that biscuit I threw overboard one night?" Toby said longingly. "Wish I had it now!"

"Now we both know how precious a sea biscuit can become," Herman muttered, almost too tired to talk. "But don't think about it, Toby. Don't think about anything— anything at all . . ." he broke off, his head beginning to throb with fever, as well as his leg.

When the first signs of morning came, Toby was ready to start on, but Herman could hardly move his leg. "I don't think I can make it, Toby," he said while they were munching their tiny ration. "You go on alone."

"I'm not going to leave you!" Toby said indignantly. "Here—eat my "lunch"!" He tried to make a little joke. "It will give you more strength."

Herman didn't want to take it, but Toby insisted. "Maybe we'll find something we can nibble on as we get farther down," he said cheerfully. "Come on; I'll help you all I can."

So they plunged into the rocky stream again, Herman staggering with pain, Toby rather giddy with fatigue and the strain of keeping both of them from a fatal slip. They kept on and on, finishing the remains of their tobacco-juice bread and lapping up a little water for their supper. Just as the sun went out of the sky and it

became dark almost immediately, as it does in the tropics, they stumbled to the bottom of the gorge and out onto the grass. It was too dark to see anything, but Toby fell flat and kissed the soil. "We did it, we're down!" he cried. But Herman was too exhausted and too ill for any feeling of joy. He crawled, groaning, into the tall grasses and lay very still, spent with pain, exhausted in every fiber of his being. Then suddenly both of them fell asleep.

It was bright morning when Herman awoke to the sound of triumphant shouts from Toby, who came running toward him waving a bunch of ripe "annuee," a native fruit.

"Food!" he called out happily. He was already eating one, and together they devoured the entire bunch of the luscious fruit. Because of their long fast they felt a little sick afterward, but the feeling passed when they started to explore and found themselves in one of the "smiling valleys" they had glimpsed from the Bay of Nukuhiva. They plunged into a shade bath under the beautiful bread-fruit trees, delighting in the cool green grove, shot through with golden sunlight. Herman had to go very slowly; he limped badly and every step was painful, but he was eager to find out where they were.

As yet they could see no native dwellings, but they knew from the plentiful growth of banana, breadfruit and co-conut trees that a village must not be far off. Toby was in the lead, since he could walk without having to stop every few minutes to rest. He tried not to get too far ahead and several times waited for Herman to catch up before going any farther with the exploration.

He had been moving steadily forward an hour or more when Herman saw him stop again, but this time there was a difference: he did not turn around and call back or beckon with his arm as he usually did; he stood stock-still, looking straight ahead, as if he were watching some-one. Herman hurried as fast as his miserable leg would allow and stole up behind Toby quietly. Without turning or uttering a word even then, Toby jerked his thumb toward the right, around a small glen.

There, in the clearing, Herman saw a native boy and girl, their small brown bodies naked except for circlets of tapa cloth around their waists. They were gazing intently toward the deep woods, alerted by the sound of the foot-steps they knew could not be those of tribesmen. They spoke no words, but after some moments the boy took the girl by the hand and they slowly advanced toward the spot where Herman and Toby stood in the shadow of the breadfruit trees.

Motioning Herman to follow, Toby went forward to meet them.

As soon as the children saw the two bedraggled sailors, they began to utter excited cries to each other, at the same time staring at the strangers with the utmost curi-osity. They did not seem to be in the least afraid—but that wasn't surprising, Herman thought. He and Toby were a sorry sight, a ragged, wretched-looking pair after their miserable journey, too worn out to frighten anyone.

When the four came face to face at the edge of the glen, the children appeared to consult with each other about what to do. Watching them, Herman noticed that they had rather light skin—a beautiful, golden tawny color—and delicate instead of broad features, as he had expected; their eyes were large and doelike. If their parents were like these children, he was sure they could not be cannibals.

Now the boy pointed toward the other side of the glen

and the girl motioned for the men to follow. They were apparently going to take Herman and Toby to their village. Hobbling as best he could, Herman brought up the rear of the little group, which soon came upon a row of native houses, built of yellow bamboo, with thatched roofs of island grasses. At the sound of cries from the children, the natives came running out, all tremendously excited by the words which, Herman supposed, must have meant "white men" as well as "strangers." He was shocked at the appearance of the men, who were hideously tattooed, with lines across their faces, up and down, including their eyelids. They were so disfigured you could hardly look at them, but the women were quite beautiful, their skin untouched except for small dots on their arms above the elbow. Whole families came out of houses and gathered around, curious-eyed, but not ferocious—though it was hard to tell from their cries whether they were pleased or hostile toward the strangers. Happars—or Typees? Herman kept wondering. Evidently the two boys were being taken to the head or chief of the tribe.

At last they came to a large building of bamboos and the children made signs for Toby and Herman to enter, the natives, by this time in droves, making a lane for them. The two runaway sailors stumbled inside and threw themselves on the straw matting that covered the floor. They were completely exhausted, and for some moments could not move. The natives poured into the house and surrounded them, and those who could not get in stood out and peered through the cane work. They were all talking and gesticulating at once, asking questions of the children, and retelling the story to each other over and over.

When Herman finally sat up and looked around, he

saw that he and Toby were encircled by eight or ten noble chiefs, squatting on their haunches and regarding the two strangers with stern attention; one in particular never took his eyes from Herman, his severe expression never changing. It was frightening, nerve-wracking; Herman wondered what to do. In desperation, he drew a square of tobacco out of his blouse and offered it, but the chief quietly motioned him to put it away.

In Nukuhiva, Herman had learned that a gift of tobacco would have made devoted friends of any of them; did the chief's rejection of it mean that he was an enemy? Was this Typee or Happar? he asked himself for the hundredth time.

Then he started, for at that very moment the chief asked the same question: "Typee—Happar?"

Herman shot a glance at Toby in the dim light, but his shipmate's face was pale and fearful; his expression showed plainly he was at a complete loss.

Herman hesitated a few seconds and then some impulse made him say, "Typee." It was a tense situation. He couldn't even glance at Toby.

The chief nodded in solemn approval and then added in a murmur, *"Mortarkee!"* a word Herman knew to mean "good."

"Mortarkee!" he repeated after the chief. *"Typee mortarkee!"*

Then what a change came over the crowd! The natives leaped up and clapped their hands and shouted for joy in their strange, weird language. Over and over they repeated, *"Typee mortarkee,"* which seemed to have settled everything. When their exuberance died down a little, the principal chief squatted in front of Herman again and, in a sudden rage, poured out a stream of violent words, not one of which the strangers could understand except the mention of *"Happar!"* over and over. Herman and Toby pretended to agree with him, every few minutes throwing in *"Typee mortarkee,"* until the chief finally calmed down and was as solemn and placid as before; laying one hand on his breast, he gave them to understand that his name was Mehevi and that he wished to know theirs.

Herman thought it might be difficult for him to pronounce his own name, and was casting around for another when his cousin flashed into his mind. "Tom," he said loudly and clearly. But the chieftains had a hard time with even so simple a syllable. They ended by adding another—he was "Tommo" to them. "Toby" was more easily caught. "Toby, Toby." They could all pronounce that.

An exchange of names in the South Sea Islands is a sign of good will; the two friends breathed a sigh of relief. For the moment, they were safe. But there could be no doubt of the fact that they had landed not in the "friendly" valley of Happar, but in the dreaded enemy valley of *Typee!*

It was hard to believe that the sociable natives, who now presented themselves individually by pronouncing their names, smiling when they heard "Tommo" and "Toby" in return, could be members of a cannibal tribe, fierce as some of them looked with their horrible tattoos, which made their faces look like masks of hobgoblins. After about an hour of "giving audience to successive troops," Herman was able to make the chief understand that he and Toby were in need of food and sleep.

Mehevi said a few words to one of the crowd, who went out and came back with a calabash of *"Poee-poee,"* and fresh coconuts, stripped of their husks, with their shells partly broken. Both young mariners drained the coconut milk in one gulp and then tried the *poee-poee,* a food made from the breadfruit tree. It was stringy, gooey and stuck to their fingers until the chief showed them how to twirl it around the forefinger, snap it off with a flick and place it in their mouths so it came off neatly, leaving the finger clean for the next mouthful. Neither Herman nor Toby was very skillful at first, but they were starving—much too hungry to worry about manners. They finished the *poee-poee* and then several other "courses" followed; some of them were delicious, all of them new and strange. They finished their meal with more coconut milk, and a few puffs from a quaintly carved pipe which was passed around the circle.

Feeling warm and refreshed, they started taking off their jackets and shirts which were still uncomfortably wet and soggy. The natives, who had been watching every movement they made with the greatest interest, made sounds of surprise when they saw the white skin of the sailors, in contrast to their faces, tanned by six months' whaling. One of them came up to Herman and touched his chest as if it had been white satin. Another bent to smell his upper arm.

Such close inspection was embarrassing, but luckily the chief began to question the white men about Nukuhiva and the French, both of whom they appeared to hate. Neither Herman nor Toby knew what they were being asked and the answers they tried to make were not understood, but once in a while they communicated a thought by gestures and the natives were delighted. At last the crowd thinned out and only the members of the household—an old warrior, Marheyo, his wife, a bevy of girls, several young warriors and a few children—were left. They brought fresh mats for Herman and Toby, put out the dim native tapers that had been flickering all evening and, throwing themselves on the floor in different parts of the long room, were soon sound asleep.

Toby, as usual, dropped off immediately along with the rest, but Herman still could not sleep because of his leg, which pained him constantly. And even if he hadn't been suffering, he could not have slept; he didn't see how Toby could lie there and snore so peacefully. They were among cannibals, they were in the hated, dreaded Typee! It was true, the natives had been kind to them, but how long would it last? Savages changed their minds from one minute to the next. By morning, in spite of their curiosity, they might have decided to do away with the two white men who had come to their village. He had half a mind to waken Toby to see if a getaway was possible. But a stab of pain even as he moved closer reminded him that he was in no shape for another flight. At last he fell asleep from sheer exhaustion. He was too tired to think about it any more.

In the morning, Mehevi came in dressed in his warrior costume—a towering headdress of plumes from the tailfeathers of a tropical bird, sperm-whale teeth adorning his ears, a girdle of tassels, and anklets of human hair; in his hand he carried a spear, with one end pointed and the other flattened like an oar blade. His face, Herman could now see, was tattooed in a pattern of triangles, and the rest of his body was elaborately marked. He must indeed be an important personage. He seemed pleased to have Herman and Toby greet him by name, and at once set about asking more questions about the "Frannee," as he called the French. For all his fierce appearance, he was most friendly.

Noticing the swelling in Herman's leg, he sent a young boy to fetch a native doctor, an old man with a long silvery beard who looked like a magician carrying a wand in his hand. He examined Herman's swollen limb carefully and all at once began to pound and pommel it as he might a piece of beefsteak!

Herman roared with pain, but the old man would not stop and Mehevi urged him on, at the same time pinning Herman's arms down so he could not move. The old man muttered some sort of chant as he pounded, probably words of healing, but the torture was unbearable. Toby went on his knees to plead with the witch doctor to stop, but he kept on until his incantation was ended. Then, while his poor patient fell back fainting from the ordeal, he produced a little sack of herbs from his belt, wet them and put them on the swelling, which he bound up with tapa cloth. It began to soothe the inflammation almost at once, but Herman was still weak with pain, rage and fright. He wanted to be left alone with Toby more than anything else, so they could talk over the situation and make plans.

The doctor and Mehevi did leave at last, but before going, Mehevi called to a young warrior, whose name was Kory-Kory, and bade him act as bodyguard to the sick man. The native seemed delighted and acted as valet and nurse as well as constant bodyguard to Herman. He was one of the most hideous of the savages, but a strong, lively and good-hearted fellow, as Herman was to discover. He insisted on doing everything for his charge, even feeding Herman with his own hand—which he took care to wash first. Then he made the patient rest most of the day. He seemed very proud of being "Tommo's" bodyguard, and strutted his authority before the young girls of the household, who gathered around, full of curiosity about the white men.

All the island maidens were slender, graceful creatures with glowing olive skin, and long curly hair tumbling over their shoulders; but there was one in Marheyo's household who attached herself to "Tommo" from the first day, and was exceptionally "beauteous." She had perfect features and strange blue eyes, and her name was "Fayaway." She was quieter than the other girls of the place, who chattered and gossiped like giddy girls in America or any country, but Fayaway, though she could be lively, had an understanding beyond her companions. She showed true sympathy for Herman's suffering and, while he slept that first day, she sat silently beside him, fanning him, brushing off the flies or insects that came near and putting her soft little hand on his feverish forehead.

The second morning Herman awakened feeling a little better and, after breakfast, Kory-Kory suggested (by a series of signs) that he carry "Tommo" on his back down to the stream for a bath. It was a welcome idea to both runaways, whose faces were still streaked from the grime of their long trek over the mountains. On the way, they were surrounded by young boys and girls who ran and capered alongside like playful animals, laughing gleefully at the sight of Herman riding "pick-a-back" on Kory-Kory. All the islanders swam—the children were like water babies, the young girls like mermaids—and they all bathed in the stream, morning and evening. They dived into the water and chased each other, shouting and splashing; they were perfectly natural and good-natured, so that Herman soon forgot his embarrassment when Kory-Kory waded out to a rock and, putting him down gently, proceeded to bathe him. Toby dove and swam with the others.

In the afternoon, Mehevi appeared once more and beckoned the strangers to follow him (Herman riding on Kory-Kory's back) to the Taboo groves of the valley, the scene of religious rites and feasts. Troops of young natives accompanied them, but when they reached the Taboo groves, the girls dropped back and disappeared— no women were allowed in there on penalty of death. Here were idols, altars for heathen sacrifices and a large building that housed aged priests, who sat cross-legged on mats all day long, deep in meditation, or stupor—it was hard to tell which from their ancient tattooed faces, grown green with age. They took no notice of the party.

Mehevi provided a huge meal for his guests, after which the pipe was passed around the circle and then, as it was nearly nightfall, they all lay down on the mats and went to sleep. Kory-Kory placed himself next to Herman, who had found the bodyguard sleeping beside him that morning; evidently Kory-Kory had had orders from the chief to stick close by his charge, and was obeying faithfully.

But about midnight Herman awoke in utter darkness to find that Kory-Kory, Mehevi and the other natives had gone; only the ancient priests lay snoring on their mats. Here was his chance: he roused Toby for a whispered conference. Where had the natives vanished? Would it be possible for the two runaways to make a second escape? they wondered in hushed tones. Then all at once they saw shoots of flame rising out of the grove, and from where they lay, they could see the figures of natives dancing around like demons.

"What can all this mean, Toby?" Herman was almost

afraid to ask.

"Oh, nothing," Toby said carelessly. "Getting the fire ready, I suppose."

"Fire!" Herman exclaimed; his heart took to beating like a triphammer. "What fire?"

"Why, the fire to cook us; what else would the cannibals be kicking up such a row about?"

"Oh, Toby! This is no time for jokes." Herman shuddered.

"Jokes?" Toby whispered fiercely. "Why do you suppose the devils have been feeding us up in this kind of style the last three days, unless it were for something that you're much too frightened to talk about?" As he spoke, they could see the forms of four islanders against the firelight approaching the building where they lay. "I told you so!" He grabbed Herman's arm. "They are coming for us!"

The two huddled in a cold sweat, spellbound with terror, as the men came in noiselessly, stealthily.

Then suddenly the silence was broken by the voice of Mehevi, in kindly tones: *"Tommo, Toby, ki ki?"* (eat), he asked softly, and another savage appeared, holding out a wooden bowl of steaming meat.

Herman's fears disappeared at once, but Toby said gruffly he was sure it was "Baked baby," and would have none of it, until Herman signaled that a light be brought. Then they saw that the fearful dish held roast pork! *"Puarkee,"* said Kory-Kory contentedly. The next day the remains of the midnight feast was sent to Marheyo's household with the visitors. The young mariners felt temporarily relieved from worry.

However, when a week went by and they were no nearer learning what their fate was to be, Herman hit on the idea of asking Mehevi's permission to let Toby go to Nukuhiva for medicine. The herbs had eased the pain in Herman's leg somewhat, but the swelling did not go down, and he was actually afraid of becoming permanently lame. Besides, the need for proper medicine was a good excuse. At first Mehevi was violently opposed to letting even one of the white men go. As kind as the Typees were to "Tommo-Toby," they seemed to be violently angry and insulted whenever either of them tried to get across the idea of leaving their peaceful valley. But finally Mehevi consented to give Toby a guide who would show him the way to Nukuhiva over a shorter route than they had taken, yet it skirted the enemy territory of the Happars.

Toby set out early one morning, leaving Herman with high hopes of his return in a few days not only with medicine, but the promise of being rescued eventually by one of the boats in the Bay of Nukuhiva. The plan was that Toby should tell their story in the harbor city and that a ship in need of hands might send a boat for them by way of a small bay leading to Typee. But at noon of the same day, poor Toby was brought back unconscious by a cluster of excited, yelping natives, who thought he was dead. He had been seen by the Happars being shown the trail to Nukuhiva by the Typee guides. As soon as he was alone, they rushed on him and one of them hit his temple with the point of a javelin. He fell from the blow and rolled bleeding back down the hill into Typee, where he was found.

After that, there seemed to be no further hope of escape. Kory-Kory stuck to Herman's side like a leech and tried with a few words they could understand to convince them they could find no better place in all the world than Typee, that if they tried to leave they would run into the wicked Happars again. Fayaway did all she could to show that she sympathized with them and wished to make them comfortable, but the young adventurers were quite discouraged.

And then, a few days after his wound had healed, Toby came running into the house of bamboos and in great glee told Herman to cheer up; he believed from what was going on among the natives that boats were approaching the bay. From outside, by means of the vocal telegraph that spread word around the valley, they could hear *"botee! botee!"* shouted from house to house in all directions. The natives began rushing to and fro, gathering coconuts, bedecking themselves with flowers and making a general commotion; meeting the boats that rarely came to their shore was a great event and they were afraid they might arrive too late at the beach, which was several miles away. Boats, when they came, never stayed long.

Toby made up his mind to go with the islanders; if he could get to the boats, he would tell the sailors about Herman and then perhaps something would be done to bring about an escape. Since Toby alone wanted to join the islanders, they all thought he was going out of curiosity, like themselves, and put up no objection. Herman complained bitterly because his lameness held him prisoner, if not the Typees, but he tried to be patient during the hours he was left waiting. Most of the village had flocked to the beach; only old Marheyo and the faithful Kory-Kory stayed with Herman.

Toward sunset the islanders began to return in small groups. Herman watched eagerly for Toby but he did not come. At last Tinor, Marheyo's wife, appeared on the pathway, followed by Fayaway, the other young girls and the young men of the house—but no Toby.

When Herman asked where he was, they seemed embarrassed. One said he would be back in a short time; another that he did not know where Toby was; and a third declared he had stolen away and would never come back. Herman was alarmed now, certain something terrible had happened that they were afraid to tell him. He turned to Fayaway for the truth; he could trust her. She made him understand, finally, that Toby had gone away with the boats, but had promised to return in three days.

It was odd—he and Toby had not agreed on any such plan. At first the young mariner thought his shipmate must have deserted him, but then reason told him Toby must have taken the opportunity to go to Nukuhiva, where he could make some arrangement himself to have Herman brought out of Typee.

Sleep came easily that night—only two days more and Toby would be back with help.

But the days passed—three, four and five days, and his friend did not return. Herman had to admit that Toby had gone away forever, leaving him to face the dangers of Typee alone. Or had he? Perhaps the savages had treacherously done away with him; it was too horrible to imagine. The natives evaded the subject of Toby entirely. They never referred to him or spoke his name; if Herman forced them to reply in answer to his bewilderment, they denounced Toby "as an ungrateful runaway, who had deserted his friend, and taken himself off to that vile and detestable place Nukuhiva."

As if to make up for such behavior, the Typees doubled their kindnesses toward Herman. Kory-Kory never left his side except to carry out his wishes. Morning and evening the faithful fellow took him to bathe in the stream, as a matter of course now; and in the afternoon, he frequently carried Herman to a particular part of the stream where the beauty of the scene had a soothing influence on him. "At this place the waters flowed between grassy banks, planted with enormous breadfruit trees, whose vast branches, interlacing overhead, formed a leafy canopy; near the stream were several smooth, black rocks. One of these, projecting several feet above the surface of the water, had upon its summit a shallow cavity, which, filled with freshly gathered leaves, formed a delightful couch." Here he "often lay for hours, covered with a gauzelike veil of tappa, while Fayaway, seated beside him and holding in her hand the leaflets of a young coconut bough, brushed away the insects that occasionally lighted on his face, and Kory-Kory, with a view to chasing away his melancholy, performed a thousand antics in the water. . . ."

When he let his eye wander along the stream, he could see native girls standing in that water catching tiny shellfish in a net, and others polishing the shells of coconuts in the water, rubbing them with a stone till they became thin and smooth, for use as drinking vessels. Still others gathered blossoms on the banks and made garlands of flowers to adorn themselves and the bamboo houses. Here and there children played, and old women washed tappa cloth in the water. It was an idyllic scene, one that made him doubt whether his kind captors could be cannibals.

In the evening, Tinor would cook special dishes for him, plying him with island treats the way his Grandmother Gansevoort plied him with sugar plums long ago. The girls of the household would chase Kory-Kory away and rub Herman's body with a fragrant oil, squeezed from a yellow root, that did much to soothe his swollen leg. Then Kory-Kory would light a pipe for him and, if no taper were burning, would make fire by friction, the only method the islanders knew for starting a fire. It took tremendous energy and was one of the hardest tasks the islanders had to perform; yet Kory-Kory seemed happy to go to the trouble if necessary, in order to please his "Tommo."

Under such thoughtful care, Herman could not help thriving and, as he grew stronger, he was allowed to walk with a stout stick for a cane. In this way, he began to explore the island. He was almost always accompanied by Fayaway, Kory-Kory and perhaps five or six others, but at least he was on foot. He sometimes liked to go to a beautiful lake into which the stream expanded and one day let Kory-Kory know that he would like to go on it in a boat. His faithful bodyguard had a canoe brought up from the sea, but when Herman wanted Fayaway to ride in it with him, the native rolled his eyes in horror. "Taboo!" was all he could say.

Herman appealed to Mehevi, who took the matter up with the old priests, and Fayaway was finally allowed to enter a canoe, free from the barbaric and senseless penalty of death. Herman Melville was responsible for a reform—he hoped, at any rate, that this action would do away with the outrageous custom.

More than two weeks passed and every day he learned something new about the Typees—their art of tattooing; their method of making tapa cloth; their cookery; (their "feast of calabashes" reminded him of a harvest festival or Thanksgiving dinner at home) their strange religious rites and ritualistic dances. The last worried him, made him uneasy in spite of the comfortable, lazy life he led:

he had no proof that the Typees offered human sacrifice to
the carven images in black stone that stood outside the
"Ti" or Temple; but one night, after a skirmish with
some Happars who had come over the hills, he heard the
natives dancing and feasting all night long. And in the
morning, he was sure he recognized the remains of a human skeleton in the calabash before one of the heathen
altars! The natives, although they satisfied his every wish,
seemed also to be guarding him, to be watching him intently, jealous of any mention of Toby, Nukuhiva, or the
outside world. Could they be readying him as a special
offering to their gods? The idea haunted him each time
he went to the Ti.

Then one day a stranger—"Marnoo"—came to the
valley, and through him Herman felt sure he could find
the means to escape. When this unusual islander—a tall,
handsome fellow, whose face was unmarred by tattooing
—came to Marheyo's, he was followed by dozens of natives, all hanging on his every word; he was apparently
giving them the gossip of the countryside and telling
amusing anecdotes. Mehevi and some of the other chiefs
arrived to hear the news also. Marnoo paid no attention
to Herman at first, but after some time walked over and
sat down on the same mat, not a yard away.

Holding out his hand, he murmured, "How you do?
How long you been in this bay? You like this bay?"

It was such a shock to hear English that Herman
could only stammer a word or two in reply. But after a
moment he recovered, and asked where the stranger had
come from. He learned that the man was from Nukuhiva,
but was welcomed here, in Happar, in Tior, and everywhere, because he was "taboo." This time the word meant
that he was outside the general rule of enmity because he

had friends in every tribe. Herman saw the chance to find out what had happened to Toby, but Marnoo claimed he did not know and seemed to evade the subject as much as the natives. When Herman asked for help in his own escape, Marnoo at first tried to persuade him to stay in Typee, but after a while agreed to do what he could.

At this point the Typees grew suspicious of the long conversation the two were having in low, earnest tones. Mehevi stood up and thundered to Marnoo to leave the house. Nothing was settled, but two weeks later the traveler returned and this time he agreed to do what he could. He even suggested that Herman try to slip out at night and come to his native village not far away, and they would go to Nukuhiva from there. But Kory-Kory kept closer guard than ever over "Tommo," and it was impossible to get away from him even at night.

In a day or two, however, word came that Toby was in a boat on the beach. It was overwhelming news and Herman was anxious to hurry to meet his friend, but the chieftains debated for some time before letting him go. Then he had to be carried on his bodyguard's back, because his leg had become worse again, probably from using it too much once he began walking again.

They were followed by throngs of natives who kept running ahead and bringing back different reports. When they were nearly at the beach, a party came up out of breath to announce that Toby was not with the boats, after all. Herman persuaded them that he must see for himself. There were angry discussions; the mob seemed to be divided as to whether he should be allowed to go down to the sea, but at last he was at the shore; and the first thing that met his eyes was an English whale boat, manned by five islanders from Nukuhiva. On the beach stood the tall figure of Karakoee, an Oahu native who had been on board the *Acushnet* several times; Karakoee had told Herman that his person was tabooed in all the valleys, just like Marnoo's.

Karakoee stood near the edge of the water with a large roll of cotton cloth in one hand, a musket in the other and two or three canvas bags of gunpowder slung over his shoulder. He was trying to bargain with the natives for Herman's freedom! Toby was not there. The message about him must have been sent to get Herman down to the beach. Now the natives began to fight among themselves whether to accept Karakoee's offer or not; a real battle took place and, in the midst of the confusion, old Marheyo, who had always been sympathetic, whispered, "Home! Mother!"—words Herman had taught him. He and Fayaway (in tears), and Kory-Kory helped him get to the boat while the mob was fighting. Karakoee followed, the rowers bent to the oars and Herman sailed away from the land of the Typees.

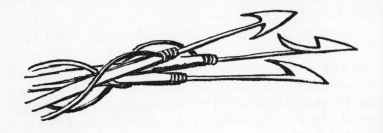

10

THE YOUNG MARINER BECOMES A BEACHCOMBER

While the boat made its way out of the Bay of Typee, Karakoee, in whose arms Herman had fallen back fainting once the excitement was over, explained that Marnoo had told him about the American sailor being held by the Typees; and when an Australian whaling ship, the *Lucy Ann,* put into Nukuhiva in search of new hands, Karakoee boarded the bark with an offer: If the captain supplied him with goods for barter, he would buy the sailor's freedom and bring him to the ship. The *Lucy Ann* lay right off the entrance to the bay, waiting for the whale boat.

166

Herman was grateful to Marnoo for having kept his promise to help; he was grateful to Marheyo, Fayaway and Kory-Kory for their part in his escape. As the boat pulled farther and farther from the valley, his joy at being released was tinged with regret at leaving the friends he had made, most of all beautiful Fayaway. He would miss her, he would miss the happy, carefree hours spent with her and Kory-Kory on the lake. There would probably be times when he would long for the pleasant indolent life he led in Typee; but no matter how kind the natives were, they had still held him captive. Remembering that, remembering the strange mysterious rites performed in the dead of night, recalling the glimpse he had had of the skeleton in the calabash, he knew he could not have remained in Typee indefinitely, no matter how easy living was there. And he knew also that he never would return.

Just now he was anxious to climb aboard the *Lucy Ann.* He hoped the fates had sent him a fair ship! However, "on approaching, she turned out to be a small, slatternly looking craft, her hull and spars a dingy black, rigging all slack and bleached nearly white, and everything denoting an ill state of affairs aboard. The four boats hanging from her sides proclaimed her a whaler. Leaning carelessly over the bulwarks were the sailors, wild, haggard-looking fellows." The picture was not too inviting, but Herman Melville was in no condition to mind. A native robe of tapa cloth thrown over his shoulders, his hair and beard uncut, his swollen leg, his body bruised from the struggle with the natives all combined to make him the object of great curiosity as the boat came alongside.

On deck, the sailors crowded around and beset him

with questions, so many and so fast he couldn't answer them all. And one young man turned out to be a "tar" he had met at the sailors' boarding house in Liverpool! It was strange the way sailors' paths might cross anywhere on the globe.

Just then he was sent for into the cabin by the captain, a cockney Englishman by the name of Henry Ventom. "He was quite a young man, pale and slender, more like a sickly counting-house clerk than a bluff sea captain." Bidding Herman be seated, he ordered the steward to hand him a glass of Pisco, which, in his state, nearly made him delirious. He hardly knew what he was saying as he related the story of his stay in Typee in answer to the captain's questions.

"D'you want to ship?" asked Captain Ventom at the end.

"Yes," Herman nodded wearily; his head felt weak and dizzy. But he added that he would like to be engaged for only one cruise, so he could be discharged at the next port if he chose. Something told him he would not want to stay long aboard the *Lucy Ann*. The captain agreed and handed him the ship's articles to sign. Then he called the ship's mate below, and charged him to make a "well man" of the new recruit—mostly because he needed his services.

The *Lucy Ann* was in need of almost everything— hands, repairs, provisions and discipline. The mate, one John German, a stout, sturdy little man with iron gray hair in ringlets all over his head, might have been a competent officer except that he drank Pisco all day long and half the time did not know what he was doing. Since the captain was sick, and not much of a seaman, it was up to the mate to run the ship, and in a more slipshod fashion no ship was ever run. He took Herman up on deck, stretched him out on the windlass to examine his leg, which he doctored with something from the medicine chest, afterward wrapping it up in a piece of old sail, "making so big a bundle that the young mariner might have been taken for a sailor with the gout."

Just after dark Herman went below into the forecastle, a dark leaky hole that proved to be worse than the crew's quarters of any ship he had sailed on so far. The bunks were built one on top of the other, fitted up with rotted blankets and placed "athwartships, at right angles to the keel," so that every time the vessel would roll, a sailor's feet went up and his head down, almost turning a somersault. Supper consisted of a battered old tin can filled with tea, leathery salt pork gone rancid, (Herman later learned Captain Ventom had purchased a load of condemned navy supplies at Sydney) and worm-eaten biscuits. Here was the problem of wretched food again, but Herman had had his fill of luscious fruits for a while and, with the first bite of stale salt pork, he suddenly felt as if he had returned to the world after having been lost in a weird Paradise.

The one saving grace of the *Lucy Ann*'s forecastle was the presence of the ship's physician, who had left the captain's quarters after a quarrel with Ventom over politics and now lived with the crew in complete camaraderie, although he had a great deal more education than any of them. "He was over six feet high—a tower of bones, with a complexion absolutely colorless, fair hair, and a light, unscrupulous gray eye, twinkling occasionally with the very devil of mischief. Among the crew he went by the name of Dr. Long Ghost, though he was listed as John Troy. He quoted Virgil, and talked of Hobbes, besides

repeating poetry by the canto." He was a man who had
seen the world and had a hundred anecdotes to tell. Then
he sang mellow old songs, "in a voice so round and racy,
the real juice of sound!" To Herman, on a ship like the
Lucy Ann, Dr. Long Ghost was "an absolute godsend."

They were to become boon companions before many
weeks had passed. The doctor, having sent in a written
resignation, gave himself out as a passenger for Sydney,
and took life easy. He ministered to sick members of the
crew who seemed marvelously content. He had little in
his supplies to heal Herman's stubborn swelling, but the
long hours of conversation with such an entertaining shipmate did as much to cure the malady as any medicine.

The ship headed first for Hytyhoo, a village on St.
Christina, one of the Marquesan islands. Here they were
to pick up eight seamen who had deserted some weeks
before; the captain hoped they would be ready to return
to duty. But there eight more men tried to desert in the
dead of night and it took bribery of the natives to get
them back. The *Lucy Ann* had captured no more than two
whales, so the crew supposed they would now be headed
for a long cruise. But they kept putting in at one island
after another, trying to sign up new hands for the battered vessel. At one island a native, Wymontoo-hee, was
lured into service on the promise of a red shirt and sailor's
cap. At another, a Maori chieftain, an Englishman whose
face was horribly tattooed and another sailor who had
run away were taken aboard. And the pale little captain
grew more sickly by the hour.

"Poor 'Miss' Ventom!" Dr. Long Ghost said sarcastically to Herman. "Our good captain should stay right
at home in his cabin the rest of the voyage." He waved
the air with his long thin hand in the direction of the

officers' quarters. He refused to take care of the captain and would not enter the cabin under any consideration.

They were now fairly at sea, though to what particular cruising ground they were going, no one knew and few cared. Two or three more were added to the sick list because of the foul conditions, but the ship sailed on as if nothing were wrong. The mate, who fought and cursed the well members of the crew—or sang songs with them, according to his mood—would tell no one where they were headed. Whaling was out of the question with so many hands invalided, but the mate insisted they were coming to a ground where the whales were so plentiful and so tame all the sailors had to do was to haul them in. Yet where this spot was, he would not say. He never reported the ship's position at noon, a custom almost all vessels observed.

Herman read Dr. Long Ghost's books, some of them yellow and tattered, listened to his stories and rested the swollen limb. He was the only one, oddly enough, who began to improve. In spite of the fact that the forecastle looked like the hollow of an old tree gone to decay and was inhabited by "myriads of cockroaches and regiments of rats" as well as the sailors, in spite of the miserable food and foul air, Herman's leg began to go down to its normal size. His lameness became less and less.

After about a month of this haphazard sailing, the captain grew so ill he never came on the quarter-deck, and the ship seemed to sail around in circles. Herman remembered what Toby had said about the sailors' superstition: "A sick captain is like a broken wheel; neither one can steer the ship straight on her course." (He wondered, as he had so many times in the past few weeks, what had ever happened to Toby, and whether he

would ever see his old shipmate again. He was very much
afraid Toby was dead.)

Within a week, two of the diseased sailors died, and
the mate came below to report that Captain Ventom was
dying. "As my name is German, he's a goner; you'd better look after him," he said to Dr. Long Ghost, and the
doctor finally agreed. He suggested that the mate head
for the nearest civilized port, and that night they were off
for Tahiti. They ran into a gale so strong it broke the
main-topgallant mast; the flying jib boom "snapped off
like a pipestem, and the spanker-gaff came down by the
run." But the ship plowed on, sailing at last into Tahiti.

Seen from the sea, the island was "one mass of shaded
tints of green, from beach to mountain top. . . . The
waterfalls flashed out into the sunlight"—it seemed to
the doctor and Herman "a land of enchantment, a fairy
world, all fresh and blooming from the hand of the
Creator."

The sight of the island was right welcome to all the
sailors, most of whom had improved as soon as they had
turned in its direction. Everybody was in high spirits;
even the sick were on deck admiring the peaks of Tahiti.
They all supposed that if the captain left the ship, the
crew would no longer be bound by her articles. At any
rate, a long stay and many holidays in Tahiti were confidently expected.

Suddenly they heard a command from German: "Stand
by to haul back the main yard!"

"What's that mean?" shouted the men. "Are we not
going into port?"

"Tumble after here, and no words!" cried the mate.
The order must be obeyed, and in a moment the *Lucy Ann*
was headed out to sea again. The men stared at each

other blankly; what would come next?

"Trouble, I'll wager," Dr. Long Ghost breathed to Herman.

They all watched while the steward brought a mattress from the captain's cabin, and spread it out in the stern-sheets of the captain's boat; next came two or three chests belonging to the master. That was enough; "a hint suffices for a sailor." They all knew that Captain Ventom meant to keep the vessel afloat while he recuperated in Tahiti.

The men became furious. The cooper and the carpenter volunteered to head a mutiny at once. And inside of a few seconds, while German was below helping the captain, "four or five rushed to fasten down the cabin scuttle; others, throwing down the main-braces, called out to the rest to fill away for the land. Things were looking critical"; something had to be done.

Herman and Dr. Long Ghost persuaded the men to stop their rash action, which would only get them thrown into irons. They held a hasty counsel of all hands on the forecastle. It took the powers of both the doctor and the young mariner to calm down the rash sailors.

"Don't you see," argued Dr. Long Ghost, "if we wait till the captain goes ashore, the ship will be in our power. Then we can take steps and bring the *Lucy Ann* to her anchors without anyone's getting into trouble!" He was able to convince them and the captain was taken ashore by the mate, who left the harpooner in charge.

That night after dinner another counsel was held. Speeches were made, fierce and fiery words let loose. At last a sailor called Long Jim stood up. "Look ye, Britons!" He pounded one fist into the other. "If, after what's happened, this here craft goes to sea with us, we are no men; and that's the way to say it. Speak the word my livelies, and I'll pilot her in. I've been to Tahiti before and I can do it." He sat down in the midst of cheers, banging of tin pans, and cries of, "Handspikes and a shindy!" "Out stunsails!" "Hurrah!" For a moment Herman thought it was all over; several of the men ran up on deck. In the noise and confusion, Dr. Long Ghost edged over to him.

"We've got to think fast," he said. "Any suggestions?"

Herman remembered a means of protest one of his shipmates on the *Acushnet* had told about. Cupping his hands, he shouted above the din: "Round robin! Let's all sign a round robin." Most of the sailors had more than once signed such a paper, which, Herman explained, could be delivered to the British consul ashore by Baltimore, the cook. "Aye!" "Good!" and "Round robin, that's the idea!" came from all corners of the forecastle, and the young mariner was told to prepare it at once.

So, using a blank page from one of the doctor's old books, lampblack mixed with water for ink, and a quill from a stuffed albatross that decorated the forecastle, Herman drafted a long statement of the sailors' grievances. He concluded with the hope that the consul would come at once and see for himself how matters stood. Right beneath, he drew a large circle, wrote "All hands" in the center of it, and sketched hands all the way around, with forefingers pointing toward the signatures to be set down. Then the sailors signed the document in a ring around the circle. That way no one could be picked as leader.

Folded and sealed with a drop of tar, the round robin was addressed to "The English Consul, Tahiti." It was handed to Baltimore, the cook, who delivered it when he took the mate back to the island with the rest of Captain Ventom's things.

It happened that the government in Tahiti was topsy-turvy at the time; the French had just forced the native queen, Pomaree, to sign the island over to them in place of the British, who up till now had had control. The British acting consul was called back to England, and a temporary consul by the name of Wilson, a missionary's son, was in charge. He knew little about governing, was not popular with the natives, and had had no experience in dealing with a crew of mutinous sailors. He came aboard the *Lucy Ann,* lined them all up and ordered those who said they were sick to be examined by a doctor he had brought along. All of these but two were declared well enough for duty—including Herman Melville, whose lameness was considered too slight to excuse him. Wilson then ordered the ship to set sail, without mentioning the round robin or any of the complaints listed in it. They were to receive whatever new provisions he could spare and were to return in three months for Captain Ventom.

The angry crew refused to accept such highhanded orders. The men refused to work, and swore they would not take the *Lucy Ann* out to sea in such wretched condition. German tried to bribe them with promises of good times to come, perhaps a share in the profits from the whale oil, but the sailors would have none of it. The battles raged, sometimes between the mate and the men, sometimes among the different groups below deck who could not agree on the next action to be taken.

There was nothing for the mate to do but take the ship into Papeete, the harbor port. The rusty anchor had hardly been dropped when Wilson came aboard once more. He lined up the "mutineers" and vowed he would

"miserably disappoint" them. When he came to Herman
Melville, the young mariner explained that he had signed
up for only one voyage and was claiming his discharge,
as stated in the articles. But Wilson merely observed
with a sneer, "You are the lad, I see, who wrote the
round robin; I'll take good care of *you,* my fine fellow—
step back, sir." And he called up the next man.

In the end, after several more "trials," he sentenced
all the members of the crew who continued to refuse to
sail aboard the *Lucy Ann* in her miserable state, to be
imprisoned in the British stockade. A few members decided to stick with German in the hopes of getting a reward, but the rest were taken to the island and thrown
into the "stocks," such as they were. It was a comic jail,
the "Calabooza Beretanee," run by a comic jailer—a fat
jovial native who went by the name of "Capin (Captain)
Bob."

Captain Bob led them along a wide, shaded road—a
beautiful avenue, built by the missionaries, that went almost around the island; in several places wooden bridges
crossed large water-courses; others were spanned by a
single arch of stone. This was the famous Broom Road,
known to all South Seas travelers; for a thoroughfare, on
which three horses could ride abreast or carriages pass
(and some had been introduced from Chili) was rare in
these remote islands. The "mutineers" enjoyed being taken
to jail with good-natured Captain Bob to lead the way
through level woods, across grassy glens or over hills
waving with palms. The scenery on Broom Road was
varied and striking, with the bright blue sea on one side
and the green mountain pinnacles on the other.

They came to a halt at a beautiful spot. "A mountain
stream flowed at the foot of a verdant slope; on one hand,

it murmured along until the waters, spreading themselves upon a beach of small, sparkling shells, trickled into the sea; on the other, it was a gleaming, sinuous thread, lost in shade and verdure." Here, on the summit of a slope, was a large native house, oval in shape, the thatch a dazzling white. "Calabooza Beretanee," Captain Bob said proudly. Dr. Long Ghost winked triumphantly at Herman: if this was the result of their resistance, the revolt had been highly successful.

Inside, the building was neither so romantic nor so comfortable as it appeared. Open all around, it was hardly more than a shed, with tufts of grass growing here and there under the roof. The stocks were long coconut boughs sawed in half down the center, with grooves for the prisoners' ankles. Captain Bob had the men gather coconut leaves to make a couch on the floor, gave them short logs for pillows and, with apologies, made them lie down so he could lock them into the stocks. He gave them each a piece of baked "taro," or turnip, to eat, covered them with a piece of brown tapa cloth, and bade them "go to sleep and be good boys." Then they were left to themselves, "fairly put to bed and tucked in!"

It was hard to sleep on your back, with your ankles locked in wooden grooves, but Herman was so worn out with the strain of the past few weeks that he was soon sound asleep. When the first light showed in the east, the fat jailer came to the Calabooza and set them loose. Leading them to the stream, he ordered them to strip and bathe, all the while beaming on them benevolently. After their sunrise bath he placed them in the stocks again, almost in tears at having to do so. Sometime later, however, he set Herman and Dr. Long Ghost at liberty, and took them to a near-by orange grove, where the trees were loaded with fruit. Giving them baskets woven of coconut branches, he told them to take back enough for all the prisoners. (He had once been to sea on a whaler and spoke an amusing dialect English of his own.) Herman and the doctor lounged under the trees, eating their fill and talking about the sea with the rotund Captain Bob; after a while, they heaped up the baskets and returned to their comrades, who hailed them with loud cheers.

Since the jail was on the Broom Road, the natives passed by many times a day and most of them stopped to stare at the prisoners, watching and commenting on every action until the men felt like monkeys at a zoo. After a few days of keeping his charges in the stocks, however, big, soft-hearted Captain Bob allowed them to be at large during the day; he asked only that they stay within hailing distance, in case the authorities came. As there was little food outside of turnips and oranges served in the calaboose, the men roamed farther and farther every day. The natives were kind to them, fed them and even offered to house them. It was a pleasant life, almost the life of an "omoo," which in Tahitian meant "wanderer" or "beachcomber." Dr. Long Ghost, who had a great appetite along with his sense of humor, bribed the sailor who brought them a daily bucket of biscuit from the *Lucy Ann,* (which they always traded for native food) to slip in a packet of salt and pepper, as the Tahitians used no seasonings in their cooking.

Just as they were beginning to enjoy the life of ease and freedom, the doctor at the consulate paid them a call and they had to run for the stocks. The physician had been charging the office for medicine and service to the prisoners, and probably felt he should actually perform some. For several days the men pretended they were ill while

he did his duty, prescribing a variety of tonics, powders and pills. Following that, they were marched back to the consulate, where Wilson and Captain Ventom, who lay on a couch still pale and seriously ill, tried to coerce them into returning to the *Lucy Ann* when she sailed in a week, or be sent to Sydney for trial there. But the prisoners were not to be bullied, and Captain Bob marched them back to the calaboose. Not a week had passed when the jailer came running in shouting, "Shippy maky sail!" They ran down to the beach in time to glimpse the *Lucy Ann* gliding past them out to sea. They were on their own!

Now there was no more daily bucket of bread and Captain Bob had not enough to feed them without something in exchange. Wilson would send nothing. They had to forage for themselves. Luckily, German had had their sea chests sent ashore, and when these were brought to the calaboose, provided all sorts of items for barter: sewing kits, marling-spikes, strips of calico, bits of rope, jack-knives and especially the chests themselves were considered treasures by the natives. It was not long before most of these treasures were gone.

September was the season for whaling ships to put in at Tahiti, and sailors on shore leave usually visited the calaboose. One of those who came suggested that the prisoners might be able to raid the ships' larders at night— they could be slipped a packet of food if they could find a canoe to get them there. Captain Bob allowed them to use his and, every night as long as the whalers were in port, two men paddled to the side of one ship or another and a bag of supplies would be slipped to them over the bulwarks.

Living in this way, getting the meals as best they could,

the little band of renegade sailors stayed on at Captain Bob's. Considered by the Europeans on the islands no more than a parcel of lawless vagabonds, they roamed the beaches and native villages enjoying the country and the free-and-easy, if scanty, existence. Tahiti had been in many ways harmed by the white men who came to its quiet shores. Civilization, although it brought some benefits, was not all blessings, by any means. As Herman and Dr. Long Ghost came to know the natives, to receive more kindness from them than from their white brothers, Herman realized that the so-called "civilized" world was far from perfect—a fact he had known for a long time, it was true, but now it was brought home to him more than ever.

About three weeks after the *Lucy Ann*'s sailing, the condition of the sailors "began to be a little precarious." Fewer ships came into port, and the natives—all but old Captain Bob—got tired of the ragged inmates of the calaboose; the novelty had worn off, especially since the treasures were gone. Herman suggested that they march to the consulate in a body and demand daily provisions from Wilson who, after all, was responsible for them. But he cut them off before they could present their case, demanding, "What do you want of me, you rascals?" And without listening, he turned and left them.

Captain Bob marshaled them back to the calaboose, where most of them decided to stay as long as they could manage to beg, borrow or steal enough food. The young mariner, however, had begun to long for a change. He had run into a couple of Yankee lads, twins; a few days before, who had deserted their ship and roved about the islands. They had last come from Eimeo, the next island, where they had been working for two foreigners who had recently started a potato plantation there. Their employers had told the twins to send over, if they could, two white men for field laborers.

Now Herman took Dr. Long Ghost aside and told him about the work to be had in Eimeo. "What do you say?" he asked.

"Everything but the digging suits me exactly," the doctor said lazily.

"I feel the same way," Herman grinned. "But it's a chance to leave the island, look over other places—and eat regularly."

So it was agreed that they meet the planters, who were coming to Papeete in their boat in a day or two. The farmers—an odd pair named Zeke and Shorty—offered to pay them $15 a month, and more if they stayed permanently. They left at midnight, in order to avoid the natives, who would have been quick to arrest the two prisoners. Bidding their shipmates a fond farewell, Herman and Dr. Long Ghost stole down to the beach where the planters were waiting with a boat, and set sail for Eimeo in the moonlight.

The potato plantation was in the valley of Martair, serene and pleasant (except for the mosquitoes, which plagued them at night) and the first day they did nothing. The planters, ex-sailors themselves, treated the new help like guests, eating, smoking pipes and talking over old times at sea. But the next morning both of them looked businesslike.

"Wall, b'ys," said Zeke, knocking the ashes out of his pipe after breakfast, "we must get at it." He was a lean Yankee from Maine and his partner was a cheerful little cockney he met on one of his voyages. "Shorty, give the doctor the big hoe and Melville the other and let's be off!"

"Right 'ere you are, boys." Shorty handed them each a crude, homemade hoe.

Herman and the doctor looked at each other, quaking. They had to work! Falling to, they hoed the stony soil until "Nooning Time." After dinner and a nap, which everyone took during the hottest part of the day, Zeke said they must all "Rise and shine," and get on with the hoeing. At his words, Dr. Long Ghost drew a very long face and declared he was not feeling well—he was too *tired*. Zeke, thinking he had worked them too hard, told them to rest and suggested that Herman and he go bullock hunting. Off they went, up the mountain.

The job with Zeke and Shorty, amusing as it was in some ways, proved too much for the two ex-prisoners of the calaboose who preferred their vagabond existence to such hard labor. After one week, Herman and the doctor turned their "backs upon the hills of Martair."

They had hit upon another scheme: they would go to the island of Taloo, where, in the village of Partoowye, the good Queen Pomaree held court, and they would try to find positions in the royal retinue. But first the two adventurers went to the village of Tamai on the shores of a beautiful lake where, the doctor had heard, the young girls danced in the moonlight, a *"hevar,"* or pagan fandango that white men were not permitted to see. They found a liberal native, Rartoo, who arranged for them to watch a midnight performance of the Lory-Lory, as it was called, a wild, ritualistic ballet; Herman had all he could do to keep the doctor from "rushing forward and seizing a partner"!

The next day they were run out of town when the respectable natives found out they witnessed the *"hevar."* So off they started for Queen Pomaree's court.

"It was the earliest dawn. The morning only showed itself along the lower edge of a bank of purple clouds, pierced by the misty peaks of Tahiti." The two barefoot beachcombers walked along the damp, spongy sand, breathing in the balmy indolent air of the tropics. Dr. Long Ghost, in great spirits, went splashing into the sea like a lanky crane, and Herman followed him. After their dip, they went on their way, light-hearted and carefree. Both the doctor and the young mariner found themselves popular among the Polynesians, treated to many a famous dinner along the route. And at Partoowye, they were taken in by a Christian native, Jeremiah Po-Po, and his wife, Arfretee, aristocrats of the village who lavished every attention and kindness upon them.

However, they could not get into the queen's presence for some time; and when they did manage to bribe their way into the grounds, their visit was unofficial. "The whole scene in the queen's hall was a strange one"; the thing that surprised them the most was the collection of "costly objects" from all corners of the globe. They started examining some of the curiosities when the attendant whispered, *"Pomaree! Pomaree! aramai kow kow."* Just then a curtain near by lifted, and from a private building a few yards away, the queen entered.

"Come on," whispered Long Ghost, "let's have an audience at once!" He was about to introduce himself when the guide pulled him back and told him to be quiet. He tried to push forward, other natives interfered, raising such a commotion that Pomaree looked up and saw the intruders. "She seemed surprised and offended."

Raising her plump arm, she issued a command to several of her women and waved them out of the house! And that was the end of their attempt to enter the queen's court.

Now there was the question of their next move. They could have stayed at Po-Po's indefinitely, but they didn't want to go on accepting his hospitality. For his part, Herman was getting tired of being a beachcomber, carefree though their life had been. Constant idleness was not for him. He wondered what was happening at home; the last he had heard, some six months before, Gansevoort had completed his law course and started on a political career. And, somewhat to his surprise, Herman "pined for the billows" again. The sea lured him, in spite of its harsh life, its injustice toward sailors.

One lone ship lay in the harbor, the *Charles and Henry,* a whaler. Herman and Dr. Long Ghost had visited her one afternoon, had talked to the sailors and heard the captain call from the quarter-deck. Herman liked what he saw and heard and, although the *Charles and Henry* had had no better luck than the *Acushnet* or the *Lucy Ann* in filling its barrels with oil, he decided to sign up as boatsteerer. Dr. Long Ghost was going with him at first, but in the end he decided he was no sailor but a "landsman." Three days later the vessel sailed and the young mariner saw his friend no more.

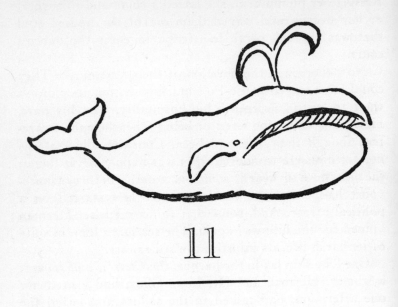

11

HAWAII

THE *Charles and Henry* was by no means new, but Herman Melville thought his latest ship was "quite pleasing. Like all large, comfortable old whalers, she had a sort of motherly look—broad in the beam, flush decks and four chubby boats hanging at the breast. Her sails were furled loosely upon the yards, as if they had been worn long and fitted easy; her shrouds swung negligently slack; and as for the running rigging, the ropes ran glibly through, as if they had many a time traveled the same road, and were used to it."

Her master, John B. Coleman, was a true sailor, not a

sickly counting-house clerk like Ventom who had tried to run his ship by conniving little tricks. If Coleman had been commanding the *Lucy Ann,* there would have been no mutiny—nor any reason for one, Herman reflected. Captain Coleman was straightforward, strong and honest. "He was an unusually tall, robust, fine-looking man, in the prime of life. There was a deep crimson spot in the middle of each sunburnt cheek, the effect of his sea-potations." He was a native of Martha's Vineyard, and from the way he called his orders, you could tell he was a sailor and no tyrant.

The ship was bound for Japan, but Herman had signed to ship as far as Honolulu. He had heard from the sailors in Tahiti that Captain Pease had put out a warrant for his arrest in Nukuhiva. He did not want to be caught and brought back to the *Acushnet;* if he could get to Honolulu, perhaps he could book passage home on a merchant ship. He was beginning to feel that he had been away long enough.

The sailors on board the *Charles and Henry* were good fellows, hearty and hale, all able seamen. The third mate, a Prussian and an old merchant seaman, was a right jolly fellow, with a face like a ruby; he reminded Herman of Max the Dutchman on the *St. Lawrence.* The captain shipped some half score of pagans at the various islands and one of these, a harpooner, was quite the most interesting sailor aboard. A native of royal blood, he was tattooed in squares, like a domino board, from head to toe; his skin had turned purple from the dye and his shaven head looked like an Easter egg with a twist of hair on top. But for all his freakishness, his black eyes had a dauntlessness that showed honesty and courage, and he was one of the bravest, most skillful harpooners

Herman had yet seen. He smoked a tomahawk pipe and worshiped a little black idol, but was in many ways more civilized than most of the sailors who were an ordinary lot, none of them especially to the young mariner's mind. Always before there had been one among the crew— Harry on his first cruise, then Toby, and last, the delicious-minded, fun-loving Dr. Long Ghost—a single soul that was like a magnet; but here there was not one that he was drawn to by common interests.

Luckily, "the skipper himself was a trump." Captain Coleman was the first master Herman had sailed with who didn't stand on quarter-deck dignity. In fact, he went so far as to be sociable, even talkative, when the young mariner was at the helm. (He had taken a liking to Herman in port, counting his pulse and declaring him to be a Yankee in every beat!)

"These is hard times, my boy," he complained one day when Herman stood at the wheel shortly after they began to cruise in the wide Pacific. "Only 350 barrels of oil after an eight months' cruise!" He shook his head despairingly. "We saw whales fourteen times on the line and only got seven of 'em!"

"Why is that, sir?" Herman turned toward the captain for a moment.

"Because they're very wild now!" The crimson spots in Coleman's cheeks grew deeper. "It's impossible for whales to be tame when there is so many ships chasin' 'em!"

"Have you ever seen the white whale—Mocha Dick?"

"Nay, but I've seen some almost as fierce these past few months. . . ." And he was off on the tale of a battle they had waged with a sperm whale near the Encantadas.

As for Herman, he was just as glad to hear that it was hard to capture whales—they would have all the sport of chasing the monsters with none of the detestable work following their capture. He liked to go bounding over the waves in pursuit; he enjoyed the wiliness of the whale, matching wits with his hunters; but splicing and rendering the long strips of blubber over the flaming try-works was never very appetizing work. It took a strong stomach to stand the smell of the bubbling oil, he realized once more when they caught the first whale of this voyage a few weeks later.

The tattooed harpooner made the kill—his throw was swift and sure. The whale had given them a merry chase and a long one; he had towed the whale boat farther and farther from the *Charles and Henry* before he turned suddenly and made such a rush at it he seemed to be standing on his flukes. The young mariner thought they would all be swallowed, when the harpooner let go his lance; and the whale fell over with a crash like the fall of a great building! He put up such a battle Herman almost wished he would win. No wonder the enormous creatures were frantic with so many ships combing the seas for them.

However, this one was taken, and Captain Coleman proceeded on his course. The *Charles and Henry* spoke many whaling vessels during the next six months—if the competition grew any greater, the oceans would be empty of oil-bearing mammals in a few decades—and at one of the gams, Herman learned that the *Acushnet* intended to stop at Honolulu for supplies. He was not going to take any chances of running into Captain Pease, so he asked Captain Coleman to discharge him at Lahaina, the first port they reached in Hawaii. Few captains could have been approached at all, but the "free-hearted Vineyarder" who piloted the *Charles and Henry* granted the young mariner's request without too much questioning.

"But we'll miss ye, lad," he said as he signed the discharge papers. "You're a nimble seaman—aye, and a thinker, too."

Herman was glad to learn he was considered a "nimble seaman" by such an able skipper. He thanked Captain Coleman for his compliments, and went to smoke a last tomahawk-pipeful with the savage harpooner, the only one of his shipmates with whom he had become at all friendly, and then it was a silent friendship, limited to nods and smiles between puffs of tobacco smoke. But Herman had great respect for the quiet strength and courage of the royal-blooded native who had left his country to see the world.

Two other sailors, John Wallace, who was ill, and Joseph Whiting were also discharged at Lahaina; and the three of them were sent to Honolulu on the schooner, *Star,* on the eighteenth of May, 1843.

Once in the capital city, Herman looked around for some sort of job. He finally heard of a dry goods merchant and auctioneer, Isaac Montgomery, who needed a clerk in a new store he was opening. It was a month and a half since Herman had arrived and he had been doing odd jobs, one of them setting up pins in a bowling alley, so he now decided to apply for a position selling calicoes to missionaries—a far cry from whaling! But he had had experience in Gansevoort's store (how long ago that seemed!) and he needed the money.

Isaac Montgomery was happy to find such a competent clerk. He drew up an agreement, which began on the first of July, to pay Herman Melville $37.50 quarterly, plus board, room and "washing." The store opened on July 13, and since they sold four yards for a dollar, they had a great run on calicoes. They were swamped with sales all day long; everybody, missionaries and natives alike, wanted to buy their goods.

"Melville, if business keeps up like this, I will make you a partner," Mr. Montgomery said when they added up the first day's receipts. He was more than pleased to have started off so well.

Herman smiled, but said nothing. He had already applied to ship on the U.S. man-of-war, the *United States*, when it sailed for home in the fall. He would work for Isaac Montgomery and study the navy rules and regulations in the meantime.

He had made up his mind suddenly. He was disgusted with what he had seen of Honolulu, where civilization had done even more harm than in the South Sea Islands. Here the natives had been degraded by the white men, turned into draught-horses and beasts of burden. Along the main streets human-drawn carriages could be seen every day—two bent-over black bodies pulling little go-carts in which sat the "superior" whites. When he thought of the kindness of the natives in Tahiti, in Eimeo, and even in Typee where he never was sure of their motives, Herman Melville was shocked at the way white men in general had treated the black, had taken away the simple happy life and substituted one of servitude for the islanders, all in the name of Christian civilization. He could not be content watching it. And he had less desire to settle down as a clerk in Honolulu than he had had in Albany years ago.

Besides, he was anxious to get home. He had finally received some of his mail in Honolulu, and there was one piece of news that disturbed him deeply. His cousin, Guert Gansevoort, now a lieutenant on the U.S. brig, *Somers,* had sentenced a young midshipman, Phillip Spencer, to

die for alleged conspiracy to mutiny. Spencer was from a
gentleman's family, of good education and not likely to
incite mutiny, although he may have protested against
injustices. There was some doubt as to his guilt, even in
the mind of Lieutenant Gansevoort, but he upheld his
decision in Washington, where the case was investigated,
by saying that he was "preserving the honour of the
navy." Guert was upset and worn out with nervous tension. Reports from the family were full of worry and
concern for his health. Herman wanted to get home and
discover all the facts for himself. It troubled him to think
that his cousin should have sentenced a man to die on
the strength of a rumor.

Late in August, when the frigate *United States*
streamed out of the harbor at Oahu with her colors flying,
she carried on board one Herman Melville—merchant-
seaman, whaleman, beachcomber, now "ordinary seaman"; and somewhere deep inside, not yet realized even
by himself, poet-writer extraordinary.

12

THE YOUNG MARINER ABOARD A U.S. MAN-OF-WAR

HERE WAS a whole new world again—the world of regimentation, of strict adherence to the line of duty, of hours regulated down to the very second and of men, 500 of them, packed into the three decks of a frigate. For a young man who had lately been a beachcomber, taking life pretty much as he chose, the change was a shock to his whole system; yet he had to adjust to it at once or be destroyed by its unrelenting sternness.

Five hundred men—when he had been used to a crew of fifteen or twenty. Five hundred men, milling around, it seemed to him the first day; they would have been a

mob if they had not been divided, subdivided and assigned
to a different post, down to the last man. When he stepped
on board, he was utterly nonplused and confused, much
more so than he had been that first morning on the *St.
Lawrence*. He had been wide-eyed then, and green; but
now he considered himself a seasoned sailor, a globe
trotter, a man of some experience. Yet here he was, "half
stunned with the unaccustomed sounds ringing in his ears."
What a tumult! The tread of armed marines, the clash of
cutlasses and curses. The boatswain's mates whistled
around him, like hawks screaming in a gale; and there
were strange noises under decks, like volcano rumblings in
a mountain. At every new, rasping sound that went ringing in his ears, he dodged as if a bomb had fallen.

While he was wondering what was going on and
whether he could stand all the noise, he was mustered into
the presence of a first lieutenant, who besides assigning
him to the starboard watch, as a maintopman, looser of
the main royal, stationed in the maintop, ready for any
duties connected with the mainmast above the main yard
—besides these instructions of duty, the young mariner
was given a variety of numbers to learn: the number of
his mess, his ship's number (for watch-roll call), his gun
number and a great many others, all of which he had to
memorize and recollect at the proper times.

"246—139—478—351 . . ." He went down the column, mumbling the figures to himself, hoping he could
memorize them all without getting his mess number mixed
up with his gun number or forgetting one of the lot.

After he received these labels, he was sent to sick bay
for his physical examination. Seated at a green baize table
was one of the assistant surgeons. He did not look up
from the reports he was reading when Herman came

in, but went on as if nobody were there. At last the young mariner cleared his throat loudly.

"Yes?" The man raised his eyes from the page, annoyed.

"The first lieutenant sent me for my physical," Herman said apologetically.

"Strip!" was the answer; rolling up his gold-laced cuff, he punched Herman in the ribs, smote him across the chest, commanded him to stand on one leg and hold out the other. "Any of your family consumptive?" he asked then.

"No, sir."

The surgeon had other questions, among them how long Herman had been ashore and how long afloat. He finished with one completely unexpected: "Are you pious?"

The young mariner was so surprised he couldn't answer for a moment, but before he had a chance, the man felt of his calves, and said, "I'm afraid you are not." It didn't make sense! But after a few more thumpings, he declared Herman "a sound animal," and wrote him out a certificate which he took back up on deck. He was ready to become a maintopman in the navy.

The *United States* was a flagship, flying the full colors of the country and carrying aboard an elderly commodore, which made her more than an ordinary frigate. There was more pomp and ceremony, more parading and visiting with dignitaries of other ships when they put in at various ports.

The sailors were called "the people" on shipboard to show they were apart from the officers, who were like the nobility with the captain as king. He—Captain Armstrong—ruled supreme; his word was absolute law. Some of the captains of whalers were dictators, like Captain

Pease, but they were more or less self-appointed. In a military ship, however, the captain reigned as if by the divine right of kings. And not Henry the Eighth himself could have been more lordly than Captain Armstrong. He was a large, portly man, bluff and hearty, and Herman never heard him speak except to command.

The "people" ate at different times from the officers. They had breakfast at eight, dinner at twelve, supper at four (the hour the captain dined) and not a bite from then on—sixteen hours between supper and breakfast; all three meals crowded into less than eight hours! It was barbarous, detrimental to the sailor's health, but it was "regulations," not to be questioned. Herman was assigned to a group, Mess no. 3, who were supposed to club their rations and take all their meals together. There were thirty or forty mess clubs on board, and their "dining rooms" were the cramped spaces between the guns on the main deck. Each week one member of the club became its "cook," that is, he had charge of the rations which came from the ship's kitchen; he prepared the pudding or "duff," which formed the sailors' dessert and was boiled in the cauldron of the ship's kitchen; and he was to see to it that his mess received its full share of food.

The sailors, all 500 of them, slept in hammocks on the "berth-deck"; eighteen inches allotted to each man! When Herman came into the berth-deck the first night, he wondered how he could possibly get to sleep in such a horde of hammocks lined up on different levels. His was the third from above; two snoring bodies were suspended above him, and one on each side, so close he could not turn in his hammock. Sleep was a mockery. The night was warm and he began to feel as if his hammock were a stew pan; lying in the moist heat, he could almost hear himself hiss!

He was glad when his watch was called, so he could get up into the fresh salt air. It was a clear, moonlit night; the frigate was gliding through the water with all her batteries. This was his quarter watch in the top and he was delighted to find that his top-mates appeared to be first-rate fellows. Whatever the rest of the seamen might be, "these were a noble set of tars," who received him as if he were a human being, and not just another "number" on the ship.

The captain of the top, John Chase, called "Jack" by all his shipmates, introduced himself first. "Make yourself comfortable," he said genially, spreading wide one arm, like a host in a drawing-room. "He was a Briton, and a true-blue; tall and well-knit, with a clear open eye, a fine broad brow and an abounding nut-brown beard . . . He was loved by the seamen and admired by the officers; and even when the captain spoke to him, it was with a slight air of respect." Herman knew at once that he was going to be friends with Jack Chase; he thanked his lucky stars that fortune had placed him under a man like this instead of some of the arrogant petty officers he had noticed already.

He looked around him. The tops of the frigate were quite spacious and cozy compared to the rest of the ship. They were railed in behind so as to form a kind of balcony, very pleasant on a tropical night like this. About twenty or more loungers were already cushioning themselves on old sails and jackets. They nodded to him in a friendly way and moved over to make a place for him.

"Melville, have you a knife I can borrow?" Jack Chase asked.

Herman reached in his pockets and handed his knife to the maintop captain, whose palm was hard from handling the ropes, but his manner was so polite and courteous, so free and easy just in asking for the knife, that Herman could tell he was a gentleman. And as the watch wore on, it was plain to see that Jack Chase was a scholar, too. He had read all the verses of Byron, and all the romances of Scott. He talked of Rob Roy, Don Juan and Pelham; Macbeth and Ulysses . . . not all at once, but little by little, with every watch Herman realized that Jack Chase was not only frank and charming, an able seaman, but a highly educated man. He could recite parts of the *Lusiad* in the original; above all things he was an ardent admirer of Camoëns, of whose classic works Herman knew very little until he met Jack Chase.

The watches, particularly the night watches, were by far the best part of the voyage for Herman. The men on the maintop were all congenial; conversation could be spicy as well as literary, and many a ballad was sung with varied harmonies. Sometimes one of them would sneak a little "grog" up there or a few biscuits. They had rare times in that top. They considered themselves the best seamen in the ship and, from their airy perch, literally looked down on the landlopers below, creeping around the deck among the guns. If he could have stayed up on the maintop among the clouds and his pleasant companions, Herman Melville would have been quite content with life on a man-of-war. But that could not be; and much as he hated to descend, he had to go down and take part in the life on—and below—decks. His duties were not limited to the maintop, no more than any other navy man's.

There was one thing he was required to do along with

all the "people" that he dreaded and loathed with all his heart, and that was to "witness punishment." On the second day out, at nine o'clock in the morning, he heard the hoarse, long-drawn-out cry echoing through the ship: "All hands witness punishment, ahoy!"

Herman started. "What is that?" he said to Jack Chase.

Jack's face was serious, tinged with sadness. "Some poor devils are being flogged."

"What for? Mutiny?"

"Lord, no— Hurry up!"—as the harsh cry was repeated. "We have to be on deck before the captain gets there."

"Why must we watch them being flogged?"

"Regulations." Jack bit out the word as they went toward the mainmast, around which the whole crew came crowding from every direction. Some seemed eager to get a good place on the booms, to be sure of a full view; many were laughing and chatting as if they were going to witness a theatrical performance instead of punishment; others were discussing the cases of the culprits; still others had sad, anxious faces, a look of suppressed indignation in their eyes; and a few were purposely keeping behind so they wouldn't have to look. Herman made no effort himself to get a front row position; he didn't know exactly what was going to happen, but an apprehensive dread came over him.

The officers all stood on one side of the mainmast, led by the first lieutenant; he was talking to the ship's surgeon, who always had to be present at floggings. Soon the captain came from his cabin with a small paper in his hand; it was the daily report of the officers. Holding up his hand for silence, he read:

"John Hall, for striking a sentry on post—twelve lashes. George Clark, for drunkenness—twelve lashes. Joseph Stanley and W. B. Ewing, six lashes with the kittens for fighting." He raised his voice. "Master-at-arms, bring up the prisoners."

A lane formed through the crowd of seamen and the prisoners came forward. Captain Armstrong examined them briefly, but gave them no chance to defend themselves. "You all admit the charge," he said; "you know the penalty. Strip!" While the sailors, with doomed expressions, started removing their jackets and shirts, he called out: "Quartermasters, are the gratings rigged?"

The gratings were square frames of barred woodwork. One of these was laid on the deck, close to the bulwarks. At a sign from the captain, John Hall, stripped to the waist, advanced and stood on the grating while one of the quartermasters bound his feet to the crossbars, and, stretching out his arms over his head, secured them to the hammock nettings above. The boatswain, who was standing on the other side, took four instruments of punishment from a green bag and handed them to his mates— every culprit received a fresh one, applied by a fresh hand. These were two cat-o'-nine-tails and two "kittens," so-called because the leather "tails" were shorter, and did not raise quite such a high welt as the "cats."

Combing out the nine-tails with his hand, the boatswain's mate swept them around his neck and brought them around with all his force on the prisoner's bare back. Again and again and again; and with every blow, the welts rose higher and higher. Herman had to look away. He remembered suddenly the "birchings" at Albany Academy, which had made him feel slightly sick. But then at least, they had been boys, and boys expected punishment from their elders, severe though that had been in Herman Melville's eyes. But this was so much worse—not only because it was heinous and brutal, cruel and harmful to the sailor's very life; but because whipping a full-grown man degraded him, made him no more than the lowest slave. John Hall was a hardened old "salt," and he stood perfectly still, but his head bowed over like an old dog beaten half to death by a cruel master.

The last one to be punished was a nineteen-year-old boy, who had never been flogged before. He was white as a sheet when he came up to the grating and he made a plea for mercy, but the captain gave the signal for the boatswain's mate to go ahead. The lad writhed and leaped under the torture of the first lash and cried out, "Oh! Oh, my God!" His white back was barred with red stripes.

It was too much. Even the toughened sailors who had seemed to be on a lark before turned serious and sympathetic. Herman quietly moved behind Jack Chase so his view was blocked and gazed out across the Pacific, dazzlingly blue in the morning sunlight; but he jumped and writhed with each lash and cry, as if he himself were being whipped. At last the punishment was over and he looked back. But when he saw young Ewing's face, his bloodshot eyes as he wept, "I don't care what happens to me now!" putting on his shirt over his blood-stained back and going among the crew, Herman resolved that he would never do anything that would bring him before the grating. He shuddered to think of it. And the men were punished for omission of duty as well as minor offenses— the slightest infraction of rules brought the lash. It was grueling enough to be forced to "witness punishment" every few days. In the fourteen months he served in the navy, the young mariner had to watch 166 floggings and he never "got used to it," as some old tars said he would.

One way to keep out of trouble, he discovered, was not to be intimate with everybody. On a ship carrying 500 sailors, over-all intimacy was bound to bring on bickerings and scrapes which too often ended with a dozen lashes at the grating. There were only a few men, besides Jack Chase and his "comrades of the maintop," that Herman came to know well. One of them was E. C. Hine, a member of the after-guard and, of all things to find on a battleship, a poet. The young mariner picked him out of the mob during the first week out, and at the oddest hours would find his friend seated in some corner among the guns—pen in hand, writing in a black notebook on a shot-box. Many of the sailors made fun of Hine, but he in turn ridiculed them in his verses which the two friends enjoyed by themselves. Jack Chase was another who befriended the poet and always took his part; sometimes Jack invited him aloft to the maintop and asked him to recite some of his verses. Some of them were very good; others needed polishing and Jack, with his good sense, taste and humanity, would gently criticize the poet, making suggestions here and there.

Hine introduced Herman to Oliver Russ, a tall, spare, Don Quixote-like member of the after-guard, whom the young mariner had noticed walking up and down by himself very often. One night during the midnight watch, while most of the men were dozing, the two acquaintances met in the waist of the ship and began to talk. That night they "scoured all the prairies of reading, dived into the bosoms of authors and tore out their hearts." That night the two became friends and kept in touch for many years after the voyage.

There was one more sailor whom Herman considered

a friend, and he was Edward Norton, "a thorough-going Yankee from Maine," not at all like Oliver Russ. Herman had started talking to Norton one evening during the dog-watch, when the sailors promenaded up and down the main deck past the guns, like people strolling on Broadway. Norton "had all manner of stories to tell about nice little country frolics, and would run over an endless list of his sweethearts. He was honest, witty, full of mirth and good humor—a laughing philosopher." When the petty problems of life aboard the battleship became unbearably annoying, Herman sought his merry friend from Maine.

It was after dinner one day during the first week at sea—August 26, his young sister Priscilla's sixteenth birthday, Herman had realized that morning—when the young mariner got his initial taste of naval combat training. The men had barely finished their "duff," which had been rather lumpy and heavy, when the ship's drummer struck up a peculiar beat—short, broken, rolling, shuffling —like marching boots. It was an ominous sound. Some of his messmates started to jump up at the opening beat.

"Sounds like a battle hymn; what does it mean?" he asked one of the others who, with groans of disgust, tried to rest a minute longer by getting up slowly instead of rushing to the summons.

"General quarters," was the answer; then, seeing Herman's puzzled expression, he added: "Sham battle."

"Oh, of course." Herman started up. The seamen, hurrying to their stations, broke into chorus in tune with the drumbeat:

"Hearts of oak are our ships, jolly tars are our men.
  We are always ready, steady boys, steady,
    To fight and conquer, again and again."

"What's your gun-number, greenhorn?" asked the messmate.

Gun number; gun number—which one was it? The young mariner ran over the list in his mind frantically. He took a guess: "478!"

"Must be the 32-pound carronades, starboard side o' the quarterdeck," said the sailor as he hurried to his own post. Men were dashing in all directions. The drum rolls grew louder, more insistent.

Luckily, Herman had picked the correct number. He was stationed at gun no. 5, nicknamed by the sailors "Black Bet." He was rammer-and-sponger of Black Bet; and ram and sponge he did, with the sweat running down his face in the August midday sun. But it was terrible work to help run the "amazing mass of metal" in and out of the porthole, especially since it had to be done in about three seconds. His stomach, still feeling heavy from the pudding, began to ache with the strain. Then, at a signal from the captain, they had to rush from the guns, seize pikes and pistols and repel an imaginary army boarding the ship from all sides. Then back to the guns. In the middle of the uproar, a loud cry of "Fire! Fire!" was heard in the foretop, and a regular fire engine played streams of water aloft. Now "Fire! Fire!" came from the main deck, and water was sloshed over the entire ship, to add to the confusion. It was a complete sham battle, even to carrying the "dead" and "wounded" below decks.

When the drill finally ended, Herman's ears were ringing, his head was throbbing and his stomach felt like lead. His shipmates were complaining, too; and the worst of it was that the call to "general quarters" usually came right after dinner. It took the flavor out of every mouthful to think that at the next moment the drum might be beating to quarters. Or if the call did not come at noon, it would be sounded in the middle of the night; and dead for sleep, you had to go through the whole proceedings. Like the cry to witness punishment, the call to quarters was an abomination to Herman till the end of the voyage.

The next Sunday was September 3, and the young mariner learned at breakfast that besides morning and evening prayers read by the chaplain on the quarter-deck, the sailors had a grand "muster round the capstan," when they passed in solemn review before the captain and officers, standing close inspection. The ceremony struck Herman as pompous; but the thing that made it suddenly terrible was the reading of the Articles of War by the captain's clerk. Thirteen of the twenty offenses listed as penal in the naval code were punishable by death! "Shall suffer death!" rang out thirteen times that morning (and on the first Sunday of every month) until Herman felt as if a cannon were being fired every time he heard those words.

By December the *United States* arrived in Callao, Peru, stopping at Nukuhiva and Tahiti on the way. At Nukuhiva, they exchanged official visits with the French frigate, *La Reine Blanche,* the very ship which had been in Tahiti when Herman Melville had been tried for mutiny with the ragged crew of the *Lucy Ann.* Wilson had put them in irons for two days on that ship. How different this visit was! He thought, too, of the first time he had stopped at Nukuhiva on the *Acushnet,* and jumped ship with Toby. Where was Toby now? And Fayaway, and Typee. He was glad they did not put in at the bay, although there was some talk of it. At Tahiti he wished he might go ashore to see if he could find word of Dr. Long Ghost, but they stopped only long enough for an official salute.

The next stop had been at Valparaiso where they lay at anchor for two weeks, and the young mariner was able to get a first-hand view of one of those cities that had seemed like legends when he heard Cousin Tom talk about them so many years ago. He had been ten years old then. The world was a very different place, he was discovering, from the fantastic picture he had formed of it at ten!

Now from Callao it was supposed that the frigate would be homeward bound; in the early evening during the dog-watch you heard the report from every group of gossiping sailors. This meant they would be facing the icy gales of Cape Horn before very long and Herman had no heavy coat, or "grego," as the men called it, to withstand the biting cold. He went to the purser's steward to ask for a pea jacket, but as the *United States* had been out nearly three years before he joined her crew, there was none to be had. So he decided to make himself a jacket.

He had practically nothing to work with; he took a large white duck sailor-blouse and, laying it on deck, folded it double and slit it lengthwise—and presto! the shirt was a coat! But white duck would never keep him warm; he would have to do something about that.

Jack Chase came along just as Herman returned with some padding he had collected. "Melville, what is this? Have you turned ship's tailor?"

"Not yet," Herman laughed. "I'm making myself a grego." He pointed to a pile of odds and ends and patch pieces he had brought from the berth-deck—old socks, old trouser legs and the like. "I'm going to pad it and sew in pockets with these."

"Oh—I thought that was your mending," said Jack.

"Laugh if you like, but I'll bet you ten pesos this jacket will go down in history," Herman defended his handiwork.

"I think it better go down to Davy Jones's locker," Jack teased him. "But seriously, Melville, I don't think it's practical. How much good will a thing of rags and patches be in the rain and snow?"

"I'm going to waterproof it with a coat of paint," Herman said calmly. And so he meant to do. But when, after several days of sewing whenever he had a few minutes of leisure, he completed his quilting, the captain of the paint room took one look at his outlandish garment and said, "Look ye, White Jacket, ye can't have any paint." He went on to explain that so many sailors had stolen paint to daub their overall trousers and tarpaulins that the paint pots were banned and put under lock and key.

Herman tried to persuade him to make an exception in this case, but the keeper of paints only said, "Captain's orders," and would not listen to any reasonable arguments. Several of Herman's shipmates happened to hear the conversation, and as sailors were always quick to pick up a nickname, he became known as "White Jacket" throughout the ship for the rest of the voyage.

At first he was quite pleased with the jacket: it was warm—a little too warm while they were in Peru; it had ample pockets for books or biscuits or pipes or whatever he wanted to stow away in its depths, and although it had a clumsy fullness, the jacket was quite comfortable. He wore it when the starboard watch had forty-eight hours' shore liberty, and he took a side trip with Oliver Russ and Hine to the near-by city of Lima. (What a strange, sad city it was—long ago half-demolished by earthquakes, its spires still leaning over, most of its houses deserted, bleached white in the sunlight, for Lima was arid, "tearless"—a ghost town. The three of them wandered around, making the acquaintance of an aristocratic old "don," who invited them to his ancient castle for wine. Afterward Hine composed a little poem: "Lima."

> "She seems a city of the dead,
> Her stately grandeur weeping fled,
> With wrinkled brow and stern—Decay
> Stands scowling o'er her ruins gray!")

Not many days had passed, however, before Herman's remarkable jacket began to give him trouble. Whenever it rained, his handmade grego soaked up water like a sponge; afterward when the sun came out, he dripped and steamed like someone in a Turkish bath. He felt weighted down when he climbed aloft. He thought of throwing his crazy-quilt coat overboard, but it was all he had.

Instead of receiving the much-hoped-for "Homeward bound" order, the *United States* was sent to Mazatlán, Mexico, for money for the squadron. Captain Armstrong received the order on February 24 and they sailed the following day. It was a bitter disappointment to those who had been expecting to go home after three years, and it meant an indefinite delay for the young mariner in finding out what had happened to his cousin.

The voyage was long and tedious. The men, most of them, were irritable, quick to take offense, quick to insult, and the resulting fights always ended up with "a dozen" on the backs of the culprits. Petty thievery was bound to happen among so many men and Herman's ample pockets were picked so many times he finally had to sew them up. Eventually his turn to be "cook" came up. He did not relish the idea, but he was determined to make a duff so delicious his messmates would never forget it. He went around getting recipes from other "cooks" of the week. He put his whole heart into mixing the ingredients and kneading the dough.

But when the pudding was boiled and the bag opened, his masterpiece plopped into the pan like lead. His messmates stared at him stonily. "Wot's in there, White Jacket? Gunpowder?" one of them said at last.

"Gentlemen, for heaven's sake! I have done my duty by that duff—I have—" He was utterly bewildered. After all his pains!

But his messmates wouldn't give him a chance to finish. "Rot!" "Tie it around his neck and push 'im overboard!" "Tell Captain Armstrong he can use it for cannon balls at next general quarters!"

For the next few meals they were very cool to poor White Jacket, who had only tried to do his best to improve their dessert. And one evening at supper they asked him point-blank to leave the mess club.

"We don't like that jacket o' yourn, anyway, White Jacket!" one of them said. "Ye're always like a wet blanket, an' it stinks."

He was spoiling for a fight, but the young mariner was not going to be snared into trouble. So, instead of giving his shipmate a black eye as he felt like doing, he got up, tucked his jacket about him, bowed and left. He certainly would not miss their company.

However, he had to belong to some mess club, according to regulations. He told his troubles to Jack Chase during the late watch that night, and the captain of the maintop said at once, "Come and join our club. We'll be glad to have you!" And the next day White Jacket was received with open arms by Mess no. 1—a "glorious set of fellows," among whom he already had many friends, including the president of the club, Jack himself. Furthermore, since there were a number of petty officers in the club, they had a permanent "cook," so that obnoxious duty was over for the rest of the voyage. One good thing, at least, came out of that miserable white jacket.

The *United States* reached Mazatlán in March, picked up the funds and left for Callao again the middle of April, but it was June before they came into port; all hands were baffled by the light head winds and calms. Captain Armstrong paced the poop-deck like a lion, and was ready to spring on any sailor for the slightest breach of rules. Nearly every day the call to witness punishment was sounded until the most tough-skinned tars prayed for winds that would send them on their way.

But finally, on the fifth of June, they made the island of San Lorenzo outside of Callao and as they rounded the Point leading to the port they heard minute guns from the U.S. frigate *Savannah*, announcing the death of Commodore Alexander J. Dallas. This meant that Captain Armstrong would be put in charge of the entire Pacific squadron until he was relieved by the Navy Department. If he had been lordly and pompous before, what would he be like now? the young mariner could not help wondering.

But the captain's promotion seemed to have put him in a generous mood. He granted more shore leaves than before and on the Fourth of July he allowed the men to put on a show. Herman's friend Jack Chase wrote and took the lead in a play, for which a stage and footlights were rigged up. Hine, as usual, wrote a poem for the occasion:

> "Far distant from that land of beauty
>   I may not share her children's joy;
> Thy iron hand, relentless Duty!
>   My every hour employs."

That particular afternoon, however, most of the sailors were "employed" watching the theatricals; only those who could not be spared from their stations did not attend. Jack Chase, starred in the role of Percy Royal-Mast in "The Old Wagon Paid Off," saw to it that "White Jacket" had a front row seat. The sailors grew wild with joy at the thrilling finish to the play, jumped up and down, hollered "Hurrah" till they were hoarse, and the officers looked on, smiling. But the very next morning, all hands were called to witness punishment and Captain Armstrong seemed sterner than ever, as if to make up for having relaxed his discipline the day before.

Two days later, the *United States* received the glorious order, "Homeward bound!" Furthermore, Captain Armstrong took command of the *Savannah* and a younger officer, C. K. Stribling, Esq. was captain of the *United States*. It was a great day for the young mariner when he heard the cries echoing through the ship: "All hands up anchor! Man the capstan!" "High die! my lads, we're homeward bound!" "Heave and pull! Unship your bars, and make sail!" When the last order was given, he scrambled to his post at the top fast as a Typee native scampering up a palm tree. Up, up, up, to loose the main-royal, so far aloft his white jacket looked like a white albatross' wing. From below he was taken for an albatross, as he

flew out on the giddy yardarm! They were homeward
bound!

Homeward bound meant they were headed toward
Cape Horn in truth this time and the jacket, which had
shrunk considerably from its drenchings, had to be length-
ened—with old canvas—below the waistband and at the
wrists. It kept Herman warm enough around the chest
and shoulders where it was well padded, but the lower
half of him came close to freezing as the ship drew
nearer and nearer the cape.

Cape Horn had tossed many a good ship, including the
Acushnet, as Herman remembered only too well; and the
United States was no exception. The days grew colder
and colder; "it was cold as Blue Flujin, where sailors say
fire freezes." The ship was becalmed for several days,
during which Captain Stribling gave an order that "All
hands skylark!" to keep them from going numb in the
cold. The decks were all the scene of pandemonium as the
sailors danced up and down, played pranks, wrestled and
boxed each other. Then a wind came up which turned into
a gale, and one stormy night when the starboard watch
had just settled into their hammocks below, the shrill cry:
"All hands take in sail! Jump men, and save ship!"
pulled the young mariner out of an uneasy sleep. With
the others, he sprang out of the hammock, and found
the frigate leaning over so steeply that none of them
could climb the ladders without hanging on for dear life.
On deck the vessel seemed to be sailing on her side. The
whole ship's company, officers and men alike, swarmed the
deck, mostly clinging to the bulwarks. The officer calling
orders—through a trumpet—shouted through the wind:
"Hard down the helm!" His object was to throw the
ship into the wind, so the topsails could be close-reefed.
The halyards were let go, but it was impossible to clew

down the yards because of the strain on the canvas. Now it blew a hurricane. The spray flew over the ship in floods. The gigantic masts seemed about to snap. "Clew down! Clew down!" shouted the officer frantically, but it could not be done. The young mariner felt as if he were having a nightmare with the ship and all its crew. Then suddenly the maintop sail was torn, and this saved the mainmast: they could now clew down the yard. The two remaining topsails were clewed down and close-reefed. Then all the maintopmen went aloft, battling sleet and rain along with the gale, to furl the mainsail. Somehow, by helping each other, hugging the yard with their arms and legs, they managed to do the deed. Herman, who had thrown off his white jacket for fear it would only hamper him, had to be carried below by Jack Chase because he was so numb when it was over. The *United States* fought the gale, set new courses, and stood due east, with the wind astern. The worst was over!

The cape was behind them and while the icy cold continued for some days (Herman hailed every snow squall, for then every sailor looked like "White Jacket"), they eventually "slid into pleasant weather." And in good time the ship sailed into the harbor at Rio de Janeiro, with the famed Sugar Loaf mountain rising behind it, so like the prints he had seen, the young mariner could hardly believe it was real. But at the sound of gun salutes, accompanied by bands playing "The Star-Spangled Banner," which came from various men-of-war in the harbor, he knew only too well that the scene was alive.

The frigate lay in Rio nearly two weeks, taking in stores and preparing for the passage home. At first the young mariner was afraid the only view he was to get of the city would be as gig-man in the captain's boat, rowing him back and forth on ceremonial visits with officers of

other ships. But Jack Chase—"noble Jack," the men
called him, petitioned for "liberty"; and with his good
friend, in company with a few other maintopmen, Herman was able to take in many of the sights he had heard
about for so long. He saw not only Sugar Loaf itself at
close range, but Singal Hill heights; they went on the
little islet of Lucia and the Isle of Snakes and walked
along the Beach of Flamingos; they visited the Charming
Bay of Botofogo and the fragrant Valley of the Oranges.
They climbed green Gloria Hill, with the belfries of the
"queenly Church of Nossa" on its crest. In the city, there
was the fine drive and promenade, Passeo Publico; the
massive arch-over-arch aqueduct; the Emperor's Palace
and the Emperor's Gardens. This was the sort of sight-
seeing he always hoped to do in port, and he considered
himself lucky to have found a set of companions who
would go along with him. Most of the men, like the
sailors in Liverpool, spent their liberty in taverns and
amusement halls. Many came back late or had to be
brought back, and received their "dozen at the gangway"
for their carelessness.

After that, the "people" were allowed no more liberty,
and while the ship lay at anchor, they thought up different
diversions. One night they auctioned off the clothes of a
sailor who had died at sea, and Herman's friend Norton
was auctioneer. The young mariner tried to palm off his
jacket, but even though Norton did his best to talk it up,
the sailors recognized it, and would have none of it.
"Ain't that the white jacket?" they cried. And one of
them declared: "I won't bid on that 'ere old bunch of
swabs unless you put up ten pounds o' soap with it."

All Norton's smooth talk could not pass off the coat
as part of the dead seaman's belongings, so the young

mariner had to take it back. And he still wore it when the nights were chilly aloft when the *United States* got under weigh the following week. During one late watch, he was so comfortable lounging in his jacket on the main-royal-yard that when eight bells sounded and his watchmates went below, he stayed on alone, musing, dreaming. He half-heard a voice calling from the "top," which was just beneath him, but he paid no attention till "like lightning, the yard dropped under" him! Coming to with a rush, he grabbed on to the tie, expecting to tumble into the ocean; but the next moment, he was standing; the yard was back in place. He was safe!

He ran down the rigging, wondering who could have done such a thing; who would make an attempt on his life? Then he heard: "Here it comes!—Lord! Lord! Here it comes! See, see! It's white as a hammock."

"Who's coming?" he shouted, springing down into the top. "Who's white as a hammock?"

The top men stared at him. They had seen a white spot up on the royal yard, and as they thought he had gone below, had taken him for the ghost of their dead shipmate. When he didn't answer their calls, they had lowered the halyards. "Bless my soul, Bill, it's only White Jacket— that infernal White Jacket again!" said the one who had been most afraid.

After that the young mariner would not wear the "infernal white jacket" again; he did not want to lose his life when he was so close to home! And when the *United States* put in at the Boston harbor, early in October, he threw his coat of many patches over the side and watched it sink to the bottom of the Charles River.

Home! He was home again after four long years of roving the seas to the far countries of the earth.

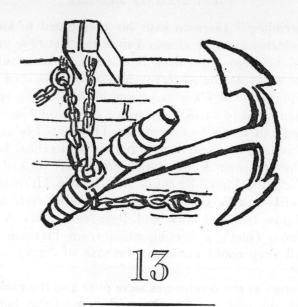

13

HE SPINS A YARN AND SELLS A BOOK

WHEN THE *United States* put into the harbor at Boston,
she was welcomed home officially by the receiving ship,
Ohio. And as Herman stood at attention in the second
row of the entire crew lined up in salute, he gave a
sudden start: one of the officers coming aboard with the
delegation from the *Ohio* was Lieutenant Guert Gansevoort! His cousin Guert—the one he had wanted most
to see!

"What is it, Melville?" Jack Chase said under his
breath, without moving his lips.

"That's my cousin—the one shaking hands with Captain Stribling." Herman kept his eyes glued to Guert's face, which was much changed since the last time he had seen him. From those deep lines he must have suffered a great deal! As the officers passed before the crew after the captain of the *Ohio* had given his welcoming speech, Herman tried to catch his cousin's eye. Now Guert had stopped only a few feet from him. He wanted to call out to his cousin, but he had to stand rigid in salute, hoping that the lieutenant would notice him. Guert seemed to be searching the lines—he must have known Herman was on board—but he kept looking at the other end. At last his glance traveled back and their eyes met! A brief nod from Guert, a fleeting smile from Herman—that was all they could exchange, because of "navy regulations."

As soon as the ceremonies were over and the ranks dismissed, the two met in a heartfelt handshake, but they still had to be formal. After Guert's "Welcome home, cousin!" and the young mariner's moving "Thank you," there was only time for Guert to murmur, "I'll notify your family." And the delegation left.

The message was sent immediately: "Herman has arrived, and you may expect him every moment."

It was fourteen days till the discharge orders came through and the crew was paid off. The young mariner had signed up for three years and had served only half his term, but since the *United States* was going to be put in dry dock for an indefinite period, Captain Stribling requested permission to discharge all the men. While they waited for word, they were kept busy "breaking out and clearing out" the ship before she was turned over to the officers of the yard.

Then, on October 14, the pay roll was called. "Herman

Melville, ordinary seaman," was part of the past and he was glad of it. Bidding his shipmates like Hine and Oliver Russ, and particularly his favorite, Jack Chase, a fond farewell, he took the money he had accumulated and hurried home to Lansingburgh.

How happy they all were to see him! And what a difference four years had made: Kathy and Priscilla were all grown up, and Tom nearly so. At thirteen, he was as tall as Herman—and longing to go to sea.

"I want to hear every single thing that happened, from the time you left Fairhaven on the *Acushnet,*" he commanded.

"Yes, yes, tell us all about it," echoed the girls. But his mother said, "Let him rest a little; he has come a long way."

It was true, Herman thought; he had come a long way. And he had changed his ideas about a great many things. As he told his adventures to an admiring family circle, whose eyes grew big with wonder at the account of his stay among the savages of Typee, he realized that he had a story to tell the world. And more important, that there was much he longed to express about his feelings toward the world and life as a whole. He wanted to write. He had to write now because he had something to say.

When he finished telling his tale, his mother shuddered and only said fervently, "Thank God you're safe at home!" But his sisters, especially Augusta, who had always encouraged her brother, even when he was doing the "Fragments from a Writing Desk," urged him to set his story down on paper. "You must write it," she said.

He didn't bother to tell her that he had already made up his mind to do so. He sat down at the little desk in his old room, where he had turned out the "fragments" nearly seven years before, and started writing. The words flowed from his pen easily now. He could scarcely put them down fast enough. By December he had already reached the point where Toby had gone with the natives to meet the boats in Typee Bay, but had not come back with them at the end of the day. As the memories of those strange days came flooding to him, Herman wondered again what had happened to Toby. Probably he would never know.

He wanted to make his description of Polynesian life as authentic as possible, and since the Lansingburgh library had practically nothing on such subjects as tattooing, or the making of tapa cloth, he decided to go to New York, where he knew there were books available. Gansevoort and Allan had opened a law office at 10 Wall Street and were living together. He could stay with them. In between his hours of work, his mother and sisters had given him all the family news. Gansevoort had become prominent in politics; he had been delivering political speeches all through the middle west as well as New York for James K. Polk, the Democratic candidate for President, when Herman came home. Now that they had won and Polk was in office, there was a chance that Gansevoort would be sent to London as secretary of the American legation. Allan was doing quite well as a lawyer. Cousin Thomas Melville had died at sea in September, only a week before the *United States* docked in Boston. Nobody seemed to know exactly what had happened to him. His death was a terrible blow to Uncle Thomas.

It was a blow to Herman also. He had been looking forward to seeing his cousin again; on the voyage home he had often thought of the pleasure it was going to be, now that he had had a few adventures of his own, to be able to spin yarns with Cousin Thomas—to swap stories of the South Pacific. Now his cousin was gone forever and he would never exchange experiences with him.

His family did not seem to know much about Guert Gansevoort, either. They could tell Herman little more than he knew already—that Guert had sentenced—or been instrumental in sentencing to death—a midshipman, Phillip Spencer, and two petty officers who had been charged with mutiny; and that he had been called to Washington to defend his decision. The inquiry had been an ordeal and a strain on him. "Aunt Mary (Guert's mother) wrote to Uncle Peter that Guert visited them at night 'almost by stealth' while the inquiry was going on," Mrs. Melville told Herman. "He was white as a ghost, coughing and I don't know what all. I guess he was nearly out of his mind wondering if he did the right thing."

Herman nodded. "He was pretty pale when I saw him—and he looks so much older! I wish I could have talked to him."

"He stuck to his decision through it all, and I for one think he was right," Mrs. Melville said loyally.

Herman said nothing. He knew his cousin must have suffered pangs of conscience. He knew how easy it was to have mutinous thoughts in the navy because of the harsh rules. He had heard many sailors express mutiny after a flogging, but they never went through with it. Had the men Guert sentenced been any more guilty than these men? He would have to wait till he had a chance to hear the whole story from his cousin.

In the meantime, he continued setting down his own tale, writing furiously in his brothers' apartment while they were in the office all day. By April the book was nearly finished and he gathered his courage enough to take the manuscript into Harper & Bros., where Mr. Frederick Saunders read it. His opinion was that "This work if not as good as *Robinson Crusoe* seems to me to be not far behind it." A work almost as good as *Robinson Crusoe* was certainly worth considering, and a council was held at Harper's, while a few blocks away the young author held his breath in suspense. Then came the dire word: The manuscript was rejected on the ground that "it was impossible that it could be true and therefore was without real value."

Herman had been dreading all sorts of objections, but not this! He never dreamed they would think his story was too impossible to be true. "How can they doubt my word?" he demanded of Allan and Gansevoort as the three finished reading the letter from Harper's. "Oh, I may have embellished the story a little," he admitted, "but not much. Most of it happened just as I told you." He suddenly looked worried. "*You* believe me, don't you?"

Yes, of course they believed him; and Allan was highly indignant that Harper's did not. But Gansevoort asked, "Is there anyone who might be able to vouch for the story?"

"Only Toby," Herman said doubtfully; "and I don't even know if . . ." he broke off with a hopeless shrug of his shoulders. There was no use in thinking about Toby.

"Perhaps some other publisher will take the manuscript without question," Gansevoort tried to console him. And Allan added, "Don't worry, we'll find some way to get the book published."

Herman was grateful to his brothers for their interest,

but he felt discouraged. It would have been simpler if the publisher had objected to his style; he could have changed it or given up writing. But to have to prove his story was true—here was an unforeseen problem. Not knowing what else to do at the moment, he took himself off to Boston to visit his father's old friend, Judge Lemuel Shaw, who had financed Gansevoort's law career. The judge had a pretty, "sympathetic" daughter, Elizabeth, whom Herman had known as "Lizzie" since childhood. Herman had called on the Shaws when the *United States* lay in port at Boston, and Lizzie had been thrilled with his accounts of the adventure in Typee. She would be most understanding about the unreasonableness of Harper's rejection. . . .

In July Gansevoort received his appointment as "Secretary of the Legation of the United States" in London. One day shortly before he left to take up his post, Thomas Nichols, the British representative, dropped into the office at 10 Wall Street. Gansevoort was not in, but Allan began to talk about the honor conferred on his brother, and from there went on to tell the stranger about Herman's seafaring career. "He got home a few months ago and has been writing something about his adventures among the cannibals. Would you like to look at it?" he finished eagerly. He wanted everyone to read the story.

Mr. Nichols had a couple of hours to spare, and thought to himself that he might as well take "the package of the sailor boy's writing" Allan held out to him. He read "Typee" at one sitting; he couldn't stop till he had finished. He had no doubt of its success; and the next day, when he took the manuscript back to the office, he advised Gansevoort to take a copy to London and have it "issued" there at the same time, or before, it was pub-

lished in New York. "I feel sure that British reviews
will make its American success," he said confidently. He
recommended several London publishers who might be
interested.

Gansevoort sailed for England on the last day in July,
and in his luggage he carried the manuscript. The first
house he showed it to, John Murray, thought the story
was "racy" and full of dramatic interest; but because it
seemed to be the work of a "practiced writer," Mr. Murray was suspicious of its "authenticity." Here was the
same objection! But Gansevoort assured them that his
brother was "a mere novice in the art" of writing, and
that he would vouch for the fact that "the adventurer
and the writer of the adventure are one and the same
person." And John Murray was so taken with the strange
story of *Typee* that he decided not to press the matter,
but to publish the book as it stood, with a few minor
omissions. By December he was talking terms and arranged to give Gansevoort a note for £100. That Christmas was a holiday Herman would long remember!

And the good news kept coming. Through the legation,
Gansevoort met Washington Irving, whose *Knickerbocker History* had earned him the post of minister to
Madrid. He read part of *Typee* to Irving, who, Gansevoort said in his letter, declared portions to be "ex-
quisite," said the style was very "graphic" and proph-
esied the book's success. And Irving suggested that it be
shown to Mr. George Palmer Putnam, the American publisher, who was in London. Mr. Putnam was delighted
with the opening chapters, Gansevoort reported, and said
that they kept him from going to church that morning.
The story had all the interest of *Robinson Crusoe*, he
thought, superadded to that of being a work of fact.

(Since a British publisher had already accepted it, he seemed to take the truth of the story for granted.) And finally, after only a few days, Mr. Putnam "expressed his desire to publish *Typee* in New York, in Wiley & Putnam's Library of Choice Reading." He came to Gansevoort's office to discuss a contract, and said the book would probably be brought out in March!

To Herman, waiting for every dispatch from London with an eagerness mounting to fever pitch when he thought about what was going on there, all this seemed much more unreal than his adventures in Typee. His book was going to be published in England and America, by two of the most important houses—that seemed more of a fantasy than the scenes in the story describing his getaway from the island, which he was writing and re-writing up until a few weeks before publication.

But it was not a fantasy, and the first copies of *A Narrative of a Four Months' Residence Among the Natives of a Valley of the Marquesas Islands* came off the press on February 21. It was favorably reviewed in *The Athenaeum*, which said: "We are sure no one will refuse thanks to the contributor of a book so full of fresh and richly-coloured matter. Mr. Melville's manner is New World all over . . ." Other magazines—*The Spectator, The Critic, The Examiner, John Bull* and *The Mirror*—carried criticisms of the book, most of them praising it. Gansevoort sent all the reviews to Herman, who drank in the words of praise with the professional thirst of any young author.

In March, the American edition appeared, under the title of *Typee: A Peep at Polynesian Life,* and dedicated to "Lemuel Shaw, Chief Justice of the Commonwealth of Massachusetts." Herman sent one of the first copies to

Judge Shaw with a letter explaining that the dedication was simple, "for the world would hardly have sympathized to the full extent of those feelings with which I regard my father's friend and the constant friend of all his family"; and said that he hoped his "little narrative" would afford the judge "some entertainment." He added, "Remember me most warmly to Mrs. Shaw and Miss Elizabeth, and tell them that I shall not soon forget that agreeable visit to Boston." (He hoped privately that the judge wouldn't forget to deliver that message; he had been thinking of Lizzie often since his last trip to Boston.)

One of the first reviews to appear was written by Nathaniel Hawthorne, who praised both the writing and the narrative of *Typee* in the language of scholarly literary criticism. Other notices followed in all kinds of periodicals, most of them favorable, but many doubting the "veracity" of the tale and quite a few taking objection to "the author's attacks against missionaries." Some compared the story to *Robinson Crusoe,* and one critic said frankly that he thought it was "in all essential respects, a *fiction* . . . from beginning to end." This might not be so bad, he went on, except that the author had "professed to give nothing but what he actually saw and heard. It must therefore be judged, not as a romance or a poem, but as a book of travels—as a statement of facts—and in this light it has, in our judgment, no merit whatever." In short, to Herman's surprise, his book created a literary furore and a sensation among the general public. As the clippings kept coming to him from both sides of the Atlantic, he was by turns delighted, astonished, annoyed and hurt. Becoming a successful author was not simply a matter of having your work accepted by a publisher, he was discovering; it had to be accepted by the readers, critics and otherwise, as well.

In the midst of the controversy, Gansevoort suddenly had a relapse of his old illness; this time it affected his brain, bringing blindness and then death within two weeks. He had worked hard and long to gain a successful career in politics and had launched his brother's in literature, but he crumpled under the strain. Herman was stunned. He knew Gansevoort was not feeling well, but he had not thought it was serious. Only two weeks before, while the word was crossing the ocean, he had written a letter to Gansevoort, trying to cheer him with various bits of news, among them the fact that *Typee* was nearly ready for a second edition; like most controversial books, it had sold out rapidly.

But he had not told his brother that he was worried about the effect of the review in the *Enquirer*—the one denouncing the book as "a fiction." He was afraid it would damage the sales and had even written an article himself, pretending to be a reader who "believed" the story, which he sent to their friend Alexander Bradford, asking him to get it published in the *Enquirer* and other papers to refute the attack. But he was not at all sure it would work; he wished there were some way of showing absolute proof that the story was true!

Now the tragedy of Gansevoort's passing drove the whole problem from his mind for a time, but when the funeral was over and the necessary adjustments made, Herman was forced to consider the best course for him to take in regard to his book. He was the head of the family now and he must do everything possible toward making a success of his career. He had already started writing a second book, based on his wanderings and adventures with Dr. Long Ghost; but how could he be sure that would be accepted any more than the first, unless he could prove that he had actually lived through those weeks in Typee?

And then a miracle occurred. On the first of July he received a clipping from the *Buffalo Commercial Advertiser*. It was a letter to the editor, which read: "In the *New York Evangelist* I chanced to see a notice of a new publication in two parts, called *Typee, a residence in the Marquesas,* by Herman Melville. In the book he speaks of his comrade in misfortune, Toby, who left him so mysteriously, and whom he supposed had been killed by the Happar natives. The *Evangelist* speaks rather disparagingly of the book as being too romantic to be true, and as being too severe on the missionaries. But to my object: I am the true and veritable Toby, yet living, and I am happy to testify to the entire accuracy of the work, so long as I was with Melville. . . . I request Melville to send me his address, if this should chance to meet his eye . . ." Underneath was the full signature, "Richard Tobias Greene."

The printed letters blurred before Herman's eyes. Toby—alive! It was like a resurrection from the dead. Toby—in Buffalo, New York; not even a state away! He sat down and wrote a letter to his old friend immediately: he would arrange to come to Buffalo in a few days, but Toby should write to him in the meantime, giving a full account of what happened when he left Typee.

Herman sent another letter at the same time, this one to Evert Duyckinck, one of the editors at Wiley & Putnam, telling him of Toby's magical reappearance; and suggesting that a sequel could be added to the second edition of *Typee,* since so many readers were concerned about "poor Toby," giving an exact account of what happened. He also said that he thought Toby's letter should be sent to the *Enquirer* and other papers as immediate proof. He himself gave it to the Albany papers, where it was reprinted the next day.

At last he was able to "show them"—all those doubting Thomases who had refused to believe his story! A few days later he took the train to Buffalo and from there to Darien in Genesee County, where Toby's father was "a respectable farmer." When the two shipmates finally met, they scarcely knew what to say, but stood staring at each other for several moments as if to make sure they were both alive. Then they both laughed triumphantly, as they had laughed when they stood on the mountain top looking down on the *Acushnet* after their escape. They felt now as if they had both outwitted fate.

"I supposed you to be dead long ago," Herman confessed.

"And I thought surely you had been eaten up by the cannibals until I saw the notice of *Typee* in the paper," Toby admitted. "As I wrote you in the letter, I was nearly out of my mind when Jimmy Fitch kept coming back without you every night, after he'd promised faithfully and I'd given him the five dollars. And then the ship sailed, and the captain wouldn't hear of turning back for you. That double-crossing Fitch!"

Herman nodded, smiling at his friend, still so intense. "Now Toby, I want you to give me all the details you can recall." He pulled a pencil and pad out of his pocket. "I'm going to take notes and write a sequel to the story for the second edition."

So Toby filled in the facts of his story, which he had sketched in the letter to Herman a few days before. When he and the Typee natives, who tried by various means to stall him along the way, finally came to the beach, they found no boats—only a grizzled old sailor, a wily Irishman, named Jimmy Fitch, who had lived for many years in Nukuhiva.

"You remember how Jimmy used to come aboard the *Acushnet* and give us all the gossip of the Marquesas?" Toby reminded Herman.

"Yes, of course," the young mariner remembered. "He wore a Manila hat, and you could read the verse tattooed on his chest through the opening of that loose tapa morning gown of his. He used to tell us some cock-and-bull stories, too!"

"That's right. I guess I should have known better than to trust him," Toby went on, "but he told me there was a ship badly in need of men, and when I wanted to go back for you, he said it would be better if he came for you the next day. He promised me he would get a force of men from the French warship to help him get you out. I still didn't want to leave you—I remember Fayaway came up and shook hands with me and said so pathetically in English, 'How you do,' the way we had taught her; and she held up three fingers, to make me come back in three days. But Jimmy was urging me and making it sound so logical that he should come back for you . . ." Toby shrugged. "I was a fool to believe him, but I did."

He went on to tell of their journey to Nukuhiva so Herman could put it all in the sequel. "When we got there, a whaler, *The London Packet,* was in the harbor, and I signed up. And Jimmy got his boat, manned by taboo natives, and pretended to go around the bay after you the next morning, but I think it was an act. He wouldn't let me go along, said it would spoil everything. Then in the evening, when you weren't in the boat with them, I was nearly frantic. I collared him and shouted, 'Where's Melville?' I was ready to strangle him, but he convinced me he would bring you back without fail the next night."

"And then the ship sailed," Herman said. He had been writing the story, almost word for word as Toby told it. "That's right. I can't tell you how terrible I felt . . ."

"When did you sail?"

"At twelve o'clock the captain came forward and gave orders to man the windlass. I went wild, but you can imagine how they paid attention to my ravings. When I came to, the sails were set and we were off on a four months' cruise." After that, Toby said, there was little more to tell. He sailed on several different whalers, always hoping to get back to Typee, but he never did. He reached home about a year after he left that fateful morning. "I can't tell you how many sleepless nights I spent," he finished. "I used to start up out of my hammock, dreaming you were in front of me, cursing me for leaving you on the island. Now it's your turn: I want to hear what happened to you after your escape."

Herman smiled. "If you wait a few months, you can read all about it in my new book." But Toby of course could not wait; Herman had to bring him up to date. The two friends spent several days together, talking, reminiscing. Then Herman went back to New York, taking with him the story, and a lock of Toby's hair, to prove he had been with his friend. (The two were to keep up an active correspondence for many years; and when Toby's first son was born, he named him Herman Melville Greene.)

Within ten days, the sequel was ready for the new edition and a good many papers, including the *Enquirer,* had printed Toby's first letter retracting their doubts and accusations. Herman wrote to John Murray in London, telling him of the lively sensation produced by Toby's reappearance, that "Truth is stranger than fiction" was on everybody's lips; on the strength of this, he suggested sending a copy of his new work to London. The story of Toby created a sensation in England as well as America, and *Typee* was reviewed two or three times in its new light by critics who had reviewed it before.

Some time in December, Herman approached the office of Harper's with his new manuscript, which he had titled *Omoo,* under his arm. Wiley & Putnam would have accepted it, he knew, but he wanted to see what Harper's would say to him now. He walked into Mr. Saunders' room feeling anything but confident. The editor greeted him cordially, but Herman couldn't tell from his manner whether he would be inclined to consider the new work or not.

"Saunders, I suppose there is no use in offering this to the house?" he remarked tentatively, pulling the package from under his arm.

"Wait a minute," Saunders said quickly. "Mr. Harper is outside in his carriage, about to go to Europe. I'll go and ask him." And he hurried out without stopping to put on coat or hat, catching the publisher just in time.

"What is it?" Mr. Harper asked.

"Another manuscript from Herman Melville," said Saunders. "He is offering it to us. What do you say?"

"Take it at once!" said Mr. Harper, jumping into his carriage and driving off.

When Mr. Saunders returned to the office and breathlessly told Herman the good news, the young mariner felt a great pride swelling within him: he was a recognized author, at long last!

14

THE YOUNG MARINER
TAKES A WIFE

Omoo was an overnight success. It was published on the
first of May, 1847, and in one week the whole edition of
3000 copies was sold out; a second edition was set at
once. The book was praised on both sides of the Atlantic;
people everywhere found it amusing, entertaining and
"more instructive" than *Typee*, as Herman's sister Helen
wrote to one of their cousins in South America. She continued, "He bears himself very meekly under his honors,
however, and to prove it to you, I may mention casually
that he is now at work in the garden, very busy hoeing

233

his favorite tomatoes." And in the same letter, she included a startling piece of news about her brother: "Herman has returned from a visit to Boston and has made arrangements to take upon himself the dignified character of a married man some time during the summer, about the first of August. Only think! I can scarcely realize the astounding truth . . ."

Yet it was true. Herman came home from his most recent visit to the Shaws engaged to Elizabeth—Lizzie, whom he had known as a small boy, when he used to call on Judge Shaw with his father. Nobody quite knew how the engagement had come about, even Herman himself. He only knew that Lizzie was kind and understanding, that she encouraged him to go on with his profession and that he suddenly wanted to settle down in a home of his own. He knew also that Lizzie would be a good wife and that her father would always be a friend. And so he had asked her to marry him . . .

Now it was June and the summer growth was beginning. He would help his mother raise and harvest the garden truck and then he would leave Lansingburgh for his own family life, perhaps in New York, the literary and publishing center of the country. On one of these mornings while he was busily working the soil, his sister Augusta brought him the mail, which had just come by the post. In it was a letter from a reader, one Dr. William Sprague, asking for his autograph! Somehow, Herman had never imagined himself receiving any such requests. He felt like Byron, famous overnight!

He put the hoe over his shoulder and started for the house. The tomatoes would have to wait; he had to grant an autograph! He sat down and wrote to the doctor at once: "You remember someone woke up one morning and found himself famous," he began. "And here am I, just come from hoeing in the garden, writing autographs." It was a wonderful feeling.

The next month brought another proof of his growing reputation as a literary figure. He was invited to tea to meet Richard Henry Dana, Jr., whose *Two Years Before the Mast* had stirred his sympathies and made him wish to rove the seas as a sailor in spite of the harshness aboard ship. That was when he joined the crew of the *Acushnet*. Now he was asked to meet the author of the work that had had such an influence on him. The rewards of his years of wandering, dreaming, pondering and finally writing were pouring in all at once.

Omoo continued to receive good notices. Readers chuckled over the antics of Dr. Long Ghost; the mock mutiny, a tragicomic picture of life aboard a whaler; the portraits of Cap'n Bob and his calabooza, Zeke and Shorty, Queen Pomaree and all the others Herman described so well. They reveled in the adventures of the two beachcombers roaming around Tahiti. One reviewer, Horace Greeley, said: "*Omoo* proves the author a born genius, with few superiors either as a narrator, a describer, or a humorist. Few living men could have invested such scenes, incidents and persons as figure in *Omoo* with anything like the charm they wear in Melville's graphic pages."

The *Daily Wisconsin,* in an editorial entitled "American Authors," said: "We perceive that *Omoo,* by Herman Melville, is obtaining so wide a success that already, *three* editions have been exhausted. . . . We trust now that Mr. Melville will consider his life as fixed—that he will live and die an author. He has the genius to succeed, and by perseverance, he may carve his name as high in the Temple of Fame as an Irving or a Scott. . . ."

Such articles brought a deep satisfaction to the young
author, and a determination to continue his career. Occasionally some magazine or paper still came out with
an attack on the truth of his stories or on the "moral
tone," which was considered loose, too free and easy to
be proper. Such criticism and worse was included in *The
American Review,* but it was answered in the *Evening
Mirror* in no uncertain terms: "We happened, like the
vast majority of readers here and abroad, to read *Omoo*
with feelings of unmixed delight. . . . But the critic
comes, and in a pet demolishes poor Omoo, calls him
a reckless liar and shameless pander, and brands every
delighted reader as a fool . . ." the article said in part
—and went on to denounce the other critic as being
guilty of the very thing that he had accused Herman Melville of doing—pandering to a depraved taste.

In the long run, however, there were more champions
of *Typee* and *Omoo* than there were assailants, and Herman was secretly pleased to be the center of such controversy. Evert Duyckinck and his brother George had
started a new monthly magazine called *The Literary
World* in February, and they printed more than one
favorable review of Herman's work. Through Evert, he
met Cornelius Matthews, who was editor of *Yankee
Doodle,* a comic weekly. He suggested that Herman write
a series of sketches for them, and in July, a month before
his marriage, he composed the first few "Anecdotes of
Old Zack," satiric pieces about General Zachary Taylor,
who was running for President. Herman's spirits were
high, and he dashed off the stories in reckless haste: his
books were going well, he had received a sizable royalty
check and he was going to be married. He pranced

through nine of the "Old Zack" articles in less than two weeks, inventing all sorts of ridiculous incidents about the general.

His wedding day was August 4. It was a soft, pleasant day, almost cool for midsummer in Boston; and Herman, who had come down from Lansingburgh with his mother and sisters, went for a walk by himself in the morning. He thought over his years at sea and wondered whether he was doing the best thing in putting them behind him. He thought of Tom, his younger brother, who had coaxed the family into letting him become a sailor and was even now somewhere on the ocean—Tom, only seventeen! If he, Herman, had remained a sailor, they might have gone out together and he could have helped his younger brother learn the ropes. But he had not gone, and this was his wedding day. As he walked along the grassy banks of the Charles River not far from the Shaws' home in Boston, his head bent in reverie, he noticed a four-leaf clover at his foot; he had almost stepped on it. This was surely a sign of good luck! He stooped and picked it carefully to take back to Lizzie. . . .

The ceremony was simple, and after it was over the young mariner, now "a married man," took his wife on a wedding trip through New England and up into Canada, to Montreal and Quebec, which neither one had seen. It was an interesting and happy journey for both of them, in spite of the uncomfortable "cars" on the railroad and the crowded, even less comfortable travel on the canal boat coming home.

When they reached Lansingburgh plans had been made for Allan's wedding to a "Bond Street beauty," Sophia Thurston, on September 22, in New York City; and it was arranged that the two brothers should buy a house large enough for themselves and their wives, Mrs. Melville and the girls. It would hardly be a home of his own, but everyone seemed so well satisfied with the idea of a joint household that Herman put up no objection. As a writer, even a successful one so far, his income was neither large nor stable, and living with the family would cut down on expenses.

And so, after Allan's "fashionable" wedding in the Church of Ascension, they all settled down in a rambling house at 103 Fourth Avenue. With so many people under the same roof, Herman had to establish some sort of routine if he was to get any writing done. He had already begun a third book, and he was anxious to get on with it. It was Lizzie who made the way easy for him. She suggested that he take a walk right after the family breakfast at eight o'clock, while she put their room to rights. When he came back, it was ready and he sat down at his desk to work while Lizzie went downstairs and kept herself busy until the bell rang for lunch at twelve-thirty. Following lunch, they both took a walk up Broadway for an hour or so, and when they came back he worked on his manuscript until dinner. After dinner he would read aloud to Lizzie what he had written during the day; and then he would go uptown to the library for an hour or so. When he came back they joined the rest of the family in the main living room for a game of cards or perhaps some reading aloud by one member of the family or another.

He could not stick closely to the routine, however, for there were often callers; his mother was delighted to be back in the social whirl of the city, making the most of Herman's fame as a writer and Allan's success as a lawyer by inviting people to the house, receiving daily calls with Lizzie and the girls, and generally running the household as she thought fit for the mother of two distinguished sons. Herman found a refuge from the company of furbelows in the home of Evert Duyckinck a few blocks away, where his friend had a well-stocked library and was more than willing to lend books to the young author.

The Duyckincks, too, were the center of a literary group to which they welcomed Herman. Here he met writers like Bryant, Bayard Taylor and many others. Once a month the gathering was only for men; they called themselves the Knights of the Round Table and they sat around discussing art, literature, philosophy and politics over a bowl of punch. Herman walked home from these evenings with his brain fired by so many ideas that he could not get to sleep. The wellsprings inside him were being sounded, and they were deep. He delved into subjects he had not dealt with before—the mystic, the symbolic and the occult. He read Spenser's *Faerie Queene,* Burton's *The Anatomy of Melancholy,* the works of Rabelais, Montaigne and Sir Thomas Browne, *Gulliver's Travels* and the popular German romance, *Undine.* He was stimulated by all these works so that he felt himself growing inside at such a fast pace that his pen could not keep up with it.

He was writing another yarn when he began this third book, another novel dealing with the "marvels of the South Seas" as Evert put it; but under the influence of the world of the mind into which he had moved, he suddenly sailed into the realm of fantasy. He had started his story on a whaling vessel, with wild but realistic characters. When their ship was wrecked by a storm, he cast them adrift in a canoe and crossed their course with that of an imaginary one bearing a beautiful maiden about to be sacrificed by the natives of an unknown island. From that point on, the story became a romance, a quest for pure love, truth and beauty, and finally, a satire on civilization—on the governments that professed one thing and practiced another. As the canoe beached at one imaginary island after another (searching for the maiden, after the hero rescues her only to have her vanish mysteriously one morning), Herman Melville sounded forth in poetic fury against the shortcomings and injustices of one country or another. He did not omit the United States—"Vivenza"—which he took to task for practicing slavery while professing freedom.

He cloaked his barbs with imagery and descriptive beauty, but the thrusts were there, just as Swift and Rabelais had used the swords of their pens to tear into the ways of mankind. *Mardi,* before it was finished, became a strange, violent, often poetic, often mystical and highly imaginative diatribe, and the young author could do nothing to prevent it. He was powerless against the budding, expanding, creative force within him. He sat in his upstairs unheated room, wrapped up in coat and shawl against the cold, and gave vent to the fire inside him. Sometimes, when Lizzie came to knock gently on his door with the word that it was near dinner time, his ink-stained fingers were numb, but he did not know it until he stopped. Lizzie spoke of "the fogs of Mardi" because its meaning was not clear to her; and when the book was published, a great many readers shared her confusion. Yet he had to write as he did, he had to get it out of his system.

He interrupted his labors long enough to go to meet Tom's boat when it docked at Westport in May, and the two brothers took great delight in comparing notes on their experiences at sea. Tom was a "born sailor," happy to have a sympathetic ear right in the family to hear the yarns he had to tell; but after a few days, when Herman had to start working on his novel again, Tom grew restless and more than ready to return to sea. His mother wanted him to settle down on Fourth Avenue with the rest of the family, but he couldn't find a job and he was bored at home.

He appealed to Herman. "You remember how it was when you came home from Liverpool; it wasn't long before you were ready to go out again!"

Herman nodded. He remembered very well, and he knew that Tom could not be happy in the already bulging household. He promised to help his young brother find a new ship, and wrote to a shipowner he had met since becoming "famous." If Mr. Parker sent the boy out in one of his ships, he would take an interest in him and promote him. Herman's success as an author, while it had not brought in much money, could at least serve as an aid to Tom!

And so it did; and when Tom had gone away again, Herman wrote furiously to finish his manuscript, adding more and more as new ideas occurred to him, until poor Lizzie, who was copying the pages for the printers, was afraid to go to Boston to visit her parents because she couldn't trust him to finish up without her. He was nearing the end, however, and he wrote to John Brodhead (one of the minister's sons he had known since schooldays), asking him to act as agent for the book; John, who had gone to London to live, had been a close friend of Gansevoort and was glad to serve as Herman's agent. He had arranged the British sale of *Omoo* after Gansevoort's death, and now, when the house of John Murray would not offer enough for *Mardi,* he took the work to Richard Bentley, who accepted it and paid two hundred guineas advance—a high price for the times.

A month before the book came out, on February 16, 1849, Herman and Lizzie's first child was born—a son, whom they called Malcolm Melville, after one of the Melville ancestors who had been a shepherd in Scotland. Now, with a child to support, Herman was more anxious than ever for his book to have a good sale.

However, when *Mardi* was published on the fifteenth of March, the critics were disappointed, puzzled and unkind in their remarks about the author of *Typee* and *Omoo* who had started out as a first-rate storyteller and had turned into a philosopher, satirist and somewhat mystical writer. They found the book tedious and boring. One British review predicted that "among the hundred people who will take it up, lured by their remembrances of *Typee,* ninety readers will drop off at the end of the first volume."

In America, where the book came out early in April, the word was nearly as bad. Evert and George Duyckinck tried to "puff" their friend's new work in *The Literary World,* but almost every other journal condemned it. Herman, although he had hoped for so much, was not too surprised. If the truth were known, he himself was a little baffled by what had happened to the tale he had begun as just another yarn. "These attacks," he wrote to Judge Shaw, "are matters of course, and are essential to the building of any permanent reputation—if such should ever prove to be mine.—But Time, which is the solver of all riddles, will solve *Mardi.*" And so he put it behind him, and plunged into another story.

This one was "nearer home." It was based on his voyage to Liverpool on the *St. Lawrence*, "a plain, straightforward, amusing narrative of personal experience," he wrote to his British publishers, "and what I write I have almost wholly picked up by my own observation under *comical* circumstances." Looking back on that voyage he could see the humor in his greenhorn blunders, his fumbling with the rigging until he got the "feel" of a ship's "rattlin's" and could spring into them like the old hands. He exaggerated the comedy of it and made himself more bungling than he had been; but he also included the darkness of the voyage in the evil character of Jackson and the foul conditions on the forecastle. He added a few adventures for color and excitement, and in the end of the book, took great delight in sending the wicked sailor to his doom in a watery grave.

He called the book *Redburn: His First Voyage,* and he referred to it as "a little nursery tale" in a letter to Richard Henry Dana and as a "beggarly Redburn" in mentioning it to Evert. He turned it out in two months, to counteract the "fogs of Mardi," and he dedicated it to Tom, who was somewhere in China by this time. He worked on the story—and on the one he started as soon as it was finished—as other men "sawed wood," merely to earn a living. Yet "Redburn" was a great deal more than a "nursery tale"; it was a first-rate novel that revealed the young writer's gift for characterization and for the *inventions* of storytelling. A writer was more than a narrator; he was a creator who saw into the souls of his beings and made them act according to his perceptions. Herman had accomplished this in "Redburn," but he had written it so quickly, with tradesmen pounding on his door for payment of unpaid bills, and babies crying in the next room (Allan and Sophia had a baby just about Malcolm's age) that he couldn't judge the merits of his work. He condemned it as "beggarly" because he wasn't sure what it was. He only hoped "Redburn" would have more popular appeal than *Mardi!*

And he did not feel much different about *White Jacket*, which he finished two months later. If the public wanted realistic stories he would give them realism. This was the tale of his years aboard a man-of-war, and he fashioned it around his own white jacket that had caused him so much misery and discomfort. It was "rather man-of-warish in style," he told his friend Dana, in that it was a militant plea for the abolition of flogging and other abuses practiced by the navy. He painted the picture as he had seen it, with all the brutality, the military pomp and ceremony, the friendships, intrigues and occasional comedy that went on in the packed world of a man-of-war. And, more important, he drew full-bodied portraits of Jack Chase, Captain Armstrong and the others he had observed closely during his months of service.

When the manuscript was completed he decided to take it to England himself; he was tired and needed a change, and he thought he might be able to arrange a better contract in person than through an agent. He asked his friend Dana for a letter to Edward Moxon, who had published *Two Years Before the Mast;* and Judge Shaw obtained notes of introduction to several important men in London for his son-in-law. On October 11, 1849, the name of Herman Melville appeared for the first time on the passenger list of a ship. Furthermore, he was a "distinguished" voyager. Captain Griswold, to whom Evert Duyckinck had introduced Herman, was a master with a literary turn of mind who honored Herman with the most comfortable cabin and gave him the run of the ship.

How different it was to be down on the passenger list instead of the crew list! If he had only been able to travel like this on his first voyage out—or if he could have changed places then with some one in "cabin class," he would have discovered that sailing in style, while it was more comfortable, was much less exciting than sailing before the mast. On this voyage there was whist in the saloon, there was interesting conversation with a German scientist, George Adler, and a Dr. Franklin Taylor— with whom he talked till a late hour on "Fixed Fate, free will, foreknowledge absolute, etc."; but there was no wild delirium of making sails fast in a blow, no rush of blood in his veins at the mate's order to "hoist the mainsail."

He wondered whether he could even climb the rigging any more. One morning he came on deck very early, and on a sudden impulse he sprang into the ropes and was halfway up inside of a few seconds. For a moment he felt the old thrill tingling inside him; for a moment he was a sailor again, nimble and strong. Then suddenly he remembered he was an author, sailing across the sea to sell his latest book for the highest price he could get in order to support his family. Little Malcolm's first sentence, spoken just before Herman left, came to him out of nowhere: "Where dat old man?"

With a thoughtful smile he ran down the rigging and for a long time stood leaning over the rail watching the blue and white waves of the morning sea.

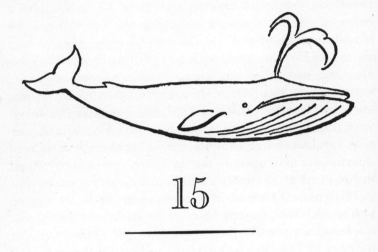

15

"ARROWHEAD"

On his first trip abroad as a traveler, author and mild celebrity, Herman visited London and Paris, where he was entertained by publishers, men of letters and people in society. He visited art galleries, cathedrals and castles. He attended the theater in Paris, where he saw the famous actress, Rachel. He took a boat up the Rhine before going back to London. Yet he was lonesome for his wife and baby, and when Richard Bentley accepted the manuscript of *White Jacket* with an advance of £200 plus fifty per cent of all editions after the first 1000 copies, he wrote in his journal, "Hurrah and Three Cheers!" and booked passage for New York.

He brought back presents for everyone—books, medallions, household gifts and toys—and after he had distributed them, in Boston and New York, he settled down to steady work on his sixth book. He had half made up his mind to write a historical novel about Israel Potter, the Revolutionary patriot and exile. He had just about run out of his own experiences as material and perhaps a figure from the past would be of more interest to the general public. Historical novels were usually popular.

But when he reached home he found that his "nursery tale," *Redburn,* had sold more than 4000 copies and that *White Jacket* promised even a larger sale, from the enthusiasm of the reviews and the orders already received by Harper's. Herman Melville was again compared to Defoe and the great writers of the sea; he was again lauded as a storyteller and an author of realism, graphic scenes and lifelike characters. Readers shuddered over the flogging episodes in *White Jacket,* and men in Washington who had been fighting for the abolition of corporal punishment in the Navy used the book as evidence for their case. A copy of *White Jacket* was placed on the desk of every Senator with the hope that it would influence them to outlaw flogging.

Richard Henry Dana sent a letter expressing his delight in both books and suggesting that Herman should do for whaling what he had done for the naval service (and what Dana himself had done for the merchant marine in *Two Years Before the Mast*). It was this, perhaps more than any other factor, that caused Herman to put aside his plans for a novel about Israel Potter and turn to his own life once more for the stuff out of which to weave the fabric of his stories. He began writing shortly after his return from Europe in January and by May he was able to send word to Dana that he was halfway through "the whaling voyage." Unexpected threads were already showing up in the pattern, however, and he added, "It will be a strange sort of book, tho', I fear; blubber is blubber, you know; tho' you may get oil out of it, the poetry runs as hard as sap from a frozen maple tree;—and to cook the thing up, one must needs throw in a little fancy, which, from the nature of the thing, must be ungainly as the gambols of the whales themselves. Yet I mean to give the truth of the thing, spite of this."

To help him "give the truth of the thing," he consulted books dealing with whale fishery, volumes about the Arctic and northern regions of the industry as well as those dealing with the southern sperm whale fisheries, which had formed the greater part of his experiences. Ever since his return from the South Seas, he had thought of the legend of Mocha Dick. Sometimes the wild stories of the white whale would come to him in dreams, when he would see the haunted, rugged profile of Owen Chase as he stood on the quarter-deck of the *Acushnet,* talking to Captain Pease. Captain Chase's jaw was set, not merely to capture whales like his host, but to track down one whale—Mocha Dick—the hated monster who stove and sank his ship, the *Essex.* It was a dread name—Mocha Dick—one held in awe by sailors all over the South Seas.

Why not use that name, along with the legends it brought to mind, as the basis for a book about whaling? Mocha Dick. . . . It was not quite right, not rhythmical enough. . . . Moby Dick! He had hit upon the exact sound he was seeking! He would use it as the title: "Moby Dick" or, "The Whale"; just as he had subtitled his last book, *The World in a Man-of-War,* he would add this explanation. Certainly the story concerned the whale as much as the man who hunted him. The whale represented a force that drove men onward against all hazards. . . .

The young author wrote at his desk in New York until well into summer; but then the heat of the city would not let him concentrate, so he took his family to Broadhall for the rest of the hot weather. Uncle Thomas had died in Galena, leaving the farm in Pittsfield to his son Robert, who had turned the mansion into a select boardinghouse for tourists who wanted peace and quiet. Evert Duyckinck, who came up for a few weeks in August, told his wife in a letter that "that nice poet Longfellow boarded here a year or two since." Across the way was Oliver Wendell Holmes's cottage, and seven miles from Pittsfield, near Lennox, was the "little red shanty," where Nathaniel Hawthorne had recently settled with his wife Sophia and their two children, Una and Julian.

With Evert at the Melville House, it was natural for gatherings and outings to be arranged among these celebrities; and on the fifth of August, the writer Dudley D. Field invited a group of men to climb Monument Mountain and have dinner at his house afterward. They met in the morning at the station house in Stockbridge— Evert, Herman and Dr. Holmes had come by "car"; their host drove them to his home, where they found Nathaniel Hawthorne with his publisher, James T. Fields. With one or two others, also connected with the literary world, they set out for the mountain top, whose rough cliffs Bryant had immortalized in one of his poems. Evert walked ahead with Hawthorne, talking of *The Scarlet Letter* with the great writer; Herman followed close behind them, listening to every word. He would have liked to join in, but he felt shy, struck into reverent silence at meeting the man whose work he greatly admired and whose meditative, almost saintly face inspired a feeling of awe. Hawthorne seemed like a spirit from the heights they were ascending; yet here he was, chatting about his book, carrying a bottle of champagne under his arm—he had been saving it for just such an occasion as this!

Before they reached the top a thunderstorm blew up, which sent them all running for shelter among the rocks. Evert described the outing in detail to his wife later: "Dr. Holmes cut three branches for an umbrella, and uncorked the champagne which was drunk from a silver mug. The rain did not do its worst and we scattered over the cliffs, Herman Melville to seat himself, the boldest of all, astride a projecting bowsprit of rock while little Dr. Holmes peeped about the cliffs and protested it affected him like ipecac. Hawthorne looked wildly about for the great Carbuncle. Mathews read Bryant's poem. The exercise was glorious. We shed rain like ducks and for wet feet—I boated about Mr. Field's parlors on the return in *his* stockings and slippers— Then came the dinner—a three hours' business from turkey to ice cream . . . Dr. Holmes said some of his best things and drew the whole company out by laying down various propositions of the superiority of Englishmen. Melville attacked him vigorously. Hawthorne looked on and Fields his publisher smiled with internal satisfaction underneath his curled whiskers at the good tokens of a brilliant poem from Holmes in a few days at the Yale College celebration."

In the afternoon the party all went off to the Icy Glen (a cavern-like break in the hills that was another sightseeing spot) and came back to Field's for tea. At ten o'clock in the evening Herman and Evert took the train back to Broadhall. As Evert commented at the close of his letter: "Mr. Field's hospitalities and kindness were of the rarest & altogether it was a rare meeting was it not—"

For Herman Melville it was even more than that. For him the entire day had been spent upon Olympus. To be in the company of such men from early in the morning until late at night, to be climbing, cavorting, laughing, dining and discussing all matter of things literary in such company was like being transported to a kingdom of the highest aristocracy of the mind, and he reveled in his good fortune. Most of all, he regarded his meeting with Nathaniel Hawthorne as one of the momentous events of his life. Here was a profound man, one whose wisdom and depth of being made itself felt whether he spoke or not. (Hawthorne was a silent man for the most part, but his was a comfortable silence, even an eloquent one; many words were not necessary with him, because when he did speak, it was always to say something worth while.) Herman knew suddenly that he wanted to stay in the Berkshire hills, that he wanted to form a true colleague and friend out of the acquaintance he had made that memorable day.

News of the excursion to Monument Mountain spread about the countryside and even to Boston, where Richard Henry Dana heard about it and commented in a letter on the "reading of Bryant's *Monument Mountain* on the very top of the original." The success of the outing stimulated others. Three days later they all gathered at Hawthorne's house, where Herman met Mrs. Hawthorne for the first time. Sophia had been a schoolteacher whose wits were keen, whose judgments were quick and usually correct. She dubbed Herman Melville "Mr. Typee," and wrote her sister that same afternoon that he was "interesting in his aspect—quite—I see Fayaway in his face."

The men explored the region around the "red shanty" and the lake it looked upon, hiking to Lennox, Stockbridge and back to the farm again before the day was over. It was after this outing that Herman wrote a criticism of Hawthorne's book of stories, *Mosses from an old Manse,* which he had begun to read three weeks before, when he first came to Broadhall. He dashed off the review between parties and excursions (Mrs. Morewood, a famous hostess of the neighborhood, who was about to buy Broadhall from Cousin Robert, was constantly planning gatherings of some sort); he did not sign his article but he put into it all the admiration he felt for Hawthorne's work and his personality. He called the piece, "Hawthorne and his Mosses," reflections by "A Virginian Spending a July in Vermont," and gave it to Evert to take back to New York the next week.

That kindly gentleman sent presents to Broadhall on his return to the city—cigars and champagne for Herman and a package of books, the published works of Herman Melville, for Mr. Hawthorne. Herman delivered the parcel, having no idea it contained his own writings. At about the same time, the *Literary World* appeared with his anonymous review of "The Mosses." When the Hawthornes received their copies, they were overjoyed, and Sophia sent a hasty, happy note to her mother: "Do not wait an hour to procure the last two numbers of *The Literary World,* and read a new criticism on Mr. Hawthorne. At last someone speaks the right word of him." And to Evert she wrote: "I cannot speak or think of anything now but the extraordinary review of Mr. Haw-

thorne in the *The Literary World*. The Virginian is the
first person who has ever *in print* apprehended Mr. Hawthorne. I keep constantly reading over and over the inspired utterances, and marvel more & more that the word
has at last been said which I have so long hoped to hear,
& so well said. There is such a generous, noble enthusiasm
as I have not before found in any critic of any writer.
. . . Who can he be, so fearless, so rich in heart, of such
fine intuition? Is his name altogether hidden?"

Her husband, also pleased but mystified, added a para-
graph or two; he had just finished reading the books
Evert had sent. "I have read Melville's works with a
progressive appreciation of the author," he began. "No
writer ever put the reality before his reader more un-
flinchingly than he does in *Redburn* and *White Jacket*.
Mardi is a rich book, with depths here and there that
compel a reader to swim for his life. . . . You will see
by my wife's note that I have all along had one staunch
admirer. . . . I must own that I have read the articles in
The Literary World with very great pleasure. The writer
has a truly generous heart . . . he is no common man;
and next to deserving his praise, it is good to have be-
guiled or bewitched such a man into praising and more
than I deserve."

The mystery of the review was not cleared up for
several weeks. In September, Herman decided to buy the
farm adjoining Broadhall, which he named "Arrowhead"
because of the Indian relics turned up in the land. Hawthorne invited him to spend a few days at the red shanty.
Herman felt deeply honored by Hawthorne's invitation,
and perhaps no week in his life meant more to him than
that one, spent largely in taking long walks with his fellow writer and in talking to him. For Herman did most

of the talking—he, who was known for his quietness and stand-offishness on shipboard, and lately in literary circles, suddenly became voluble and went on at a great rate about his ideas on a hundred subjects, while Nathaniel Hawthorne listened thoughtfully.

One of the first things to come out was Herman's confession that it was he who had written the remarkable review Sophia had been raving about. She immediately sent the news to her mother in a letter that was to mark her one of the most clear-seeing women of all time. She was bubbling over with enthusiasm for their new friend, colleague and neighbor. "We have discovered who wrote the Review in *The Literary World*. It was none other than Herman Melville himself! I had some delightful conversations with him about the 'sweetest Man of Mosses' after we discovered him to be the author of the Review. . . . He said Mr. Hawthorne was the first person whose physical being appeared to him wholly in harmony with the intellectual & spiritual. He said the sunny hair & the pensiveness, the symmetry of his face, the depth of eyes, 'the gleam,—the shadow—& the peace supreme' all were in exact response to the high calm intellect, the glowing deep heart—the purity of actual and spiritual life. *Mr.* Melville is a person of great ardor and simplicity. He is all on fire with the subject that interests him. It rings through his frame like a cathedral bell. His truth and honesty shine out at every point. At the same time he sees things artistically, as you perceive in his books. . . . He was very careful not to interrupt Mr. Hawthorne's mornings when he was here. He generally walked off somewhere—and one morning he shut himself into the boudoir and read Mr. Emerson's Essays. . . . In the afternoon he walked with Mr. Hawthorne

. . . He said Mr. Hawthorne's great but hospitable silence drew him out—that it was astonishing how *sociable* his silence was. (This Mr. Emerson used to feel.) He said sometimes they would walk along without talking on either side, but that even then they seemed to be very social . . ."

One moonlight night shortly after she wrote this, Herman drove up in his carriage to announce that he had closed the deal on the farm and that he expected to move his family up to the country in a few weeks. His closest neighbors would be the Moreheads, and the Hawthornes were within walking distance if he chose to hike. He was elated at the thought of living in the country again, so near the writer he most revered.

"Some day I shall tear down the barn on the hill and build a towered house there," he boasted.

The Hawthornes laughed, and Sophia asked, "How do you mean that?"

"Literally. I intend to put up an actual tower!" he assured them. At that moment he felt able to build it himself.

Then young Julian Hawthorne, who was listening from a corner, asked "Mr. Melville" to tell them a story of the South Seas, and he was off on a yarn that made them see Fayaway, Kory-Kory or old Mow-Mow, the one-eyed chief, whichever one he was impersonating. He found he could act out his stories in front of the Hawthornes, he felt so at ease with them. And they, for their part, thought him "very agreeable and entertaining," as Mrs. Hawthorne said.

She went on to describe him as a "man with a true warm heart, and a soul and an intellect—with life to his fingertips; earnest, sincere, and reverent; very tender and *modest*. And I am not sure that he is not a very great man; but I have not quite decided upon my own opinion. He has very keen perceptive power; but what astonishes me is, that his eyes are not large and deep. He seems to see everything very accurately; and how he can do so with his small eyes, I cannot tell. They are not keen eyes, either, but quite undistinguished in any way. His nose is straight and rather handsome, his mouth expressive of sensibility and emotion. He is tall and erect, with an air free, brave, and manly. When conversing, he is full of gesture and force, and loses himself in his subject. . . . Once in a while, his animation gives place to a singularly quiet expression, out of these eyes to which I have objected; an indrawn, dim look, but which at the same time makes you feel that he is at that instant taking deepest note of what is before him. It is a strange, lazy glance, but with a power in it quite unique. It does not seem to penetrate through you, but to take you into himself. I saw him look at Una so, yesterday, several times."

Her portrait of the author of *Moby Dick* was one of the few ever to be sketched of him; and Herman would have been astonished if he had read the glowing terms she used to describe him. He knew that the Hawthornes had been hospitable and kind to him and that he considered them—Mr. Hawthorne especially—the finest, most extraordinary of friends; but he had no idea that either one of them thought enough of him to discuss him at such length or in such complimentary words. It would have given him much happiness if he had seen Mrs. Hawthorne's letter; he never knew the tribute she paid him.

Toward the end of September, he moved his family, including his mother and sisters, to Pittsfield; Allan stayed on in New York because of his law practice. Since Her-

man was now the oldest son, Mrs. Melville thought she
and the girls should go with him to Arrowhead, forming
what Augusta called a "daughter-full" household. By October they were established in the farmhouse, and Herman was writing to Evert about the "harvest" of apples.
His friend had sent him a piece of news that made his
heart leap up with joy and pride. "Thank you for your letter with the paper the other day," he said. "I am offering
my devout jubilations for the abolition of the flogging
law."

He did not know how great a part *White Jacket* had
actually played in doing away with the cruel practice, but
he was glad now that he had been so outspoken; and he
was deeply grateful at the thought that men in the Navy
would no longer have to suffer such pain and degradation.
Any experience, no matter how horrifying, could be turned
to good account if you were a writer and a thoughtful
person; and Herman meant to apply this principle as well
as his powers of imagination in the book he was trying to
complete about the great white whale.

When Evert was there in August, he had written to his
wife: "Melville has a new book mostly done—a romantic,
fanciful & literal & most enjoyable presentation of the
whale fishery. . . ." But the manuscript was a long way
from being done, especially since Herman kept developing
its theme, adding more and more scenes which increased
its length. As winter settled down around them like a
blanket, he dove deeper and deeper into the story of the
quest for the whale, and its hidden meaning. "I have a
sort of sea-feeling here in the country, now that the
ground is all covered with snow," he said in a letter to
Evert in mid-December. "I look out of my window in
the morning when I rise as I would out of a port-hole of

a ship in the Atlantic. My room seems a ship's cabin; & at nights when I wake up and hear the wind shrieking, I almost fancy there is too much sail on the house, & I had better go on the roof and rig in the chimney.

"Do you want to know how I pass my time? I rise at eight—& go to the barn—say good-morning to the horse, & give him his breakfast. (It goes to my heart to give him a cold one, but it can't be helped.) Then, pay a visit to my cow—cut up a pumpkin or two for her, & stand by to see her eat it—for it's a pleasant sight to see a cow move her jaws—she does it so mildly and with such a sanctity. My own breakfast over, I go to my work-room and light my fire—then spread my Mss. on the table—take one business squint at it, & fall to with a will. At 2½ P. M. I hear a knock at my door, which serves to wean me from my writing, however interested I may be. My friends the horse and cow now demand their dinner—and I go and give it them. My own dinner over, I rig my sleigh, and with my mother or sisters start off for the village. . . . My evenings I spend in a sort of mesmeric state in my room—not being able to read—only now and then skimming over some large-printed book. Can you send me about fifty fast-writing youths, with an easy style & not averse to polishing their labors? If you can, I wish you would, because since I have been here I have planned about that number of future works and can't find enough time to think about them separately.—But I don't know but a book in a man's brain is better off than a book bound in calf—at any rate it is safer from criticism. And taking a book off the brain, is akin to the ticklish and dangerous business of taking an old painting off a panel —you have to scrape off the whole brain in order to get at it with due safety—& even then, the painting may not be worth the trouble."

He often wondered whether the "painting" of a whaling voyage he was "taking off his brain" would be worth the trouble it was giving him—not so much in the writing, for the scenes came swiftly, but he was disturbed by the direction in which the story was moving; and as in *Mardi* he was powerless to stop it. Yet he did have more control this time. He was able to fuse the real with the fantastic so that it was all of one piece. The story did not start out as one thing and then become another. Herman Melville, the erstwhile mariner turned author, picked his crew from all the races of the earth; none like it was ever before gathered together on one ship. It was a composite of all the crews he had seen and mingled with, harpooners he had known (like the Maori chieftain, or the Indian who smoked a tomahawk), but these men also represented the different civilizations that peopled the globe. And the whaling vessel itself, which he christened *The Pequod* (instead of the *Essex* or any of the other ships that Mocha Dick had sunk) was doomed to destruction from the start. He made the story dramatic and tense, like a Greek tragedy.

All through the winter he worked, interrupting his labors only now and then to pay the Hawthornes a call or, on one or two occasions, to receive a visit from the older author, who drove his sleigh, once with Una and once by himself, to spend the day at "Arrowhead." On one of Herman's visits, Sophia gave him an engraving made from the latest portrait of her husband, which had been painted by Thompson. In it Mr. Hawthorne looked melancholy and contemplative and rather lofty; the indescribable quality of sunshine usually in his expression was lacking, but Herman considered it a great honor to receive the engraving, which he prized all his life.

Late in the spring he was writing to his friend to say that the "Whale" was driving through the press and that he was going to New York to see it through while he completed the last few chapters. He had put into his book the details of whaling industry, from the thrill of the chase to the stripping and the firing of the try-pots; he had shown the life of whalemen just as he had of Navy men. But he had used the world of whaling only as a framework to show the driving forces in men's lives, the motives which caused them to rush on and on toward their goal. The whale himself was a force, and as the story was nearing its close, Herman put in his letter to Hawthorne: "As the fisherman says, 'he's in his flurry'. . . . I'm going to take him by his jaw, however, before long, and finish him up in some fashion or other." And later on he wrote: "Shall I send you a fin of the 'Whale' by way of a specimen mouthful? The tail is not yet cooked, though the hell-fire in which the whole book is broiled might not unreasonably have cooked it ere this."

Then the activities of the summer began, haying season on the farm and visiting season in the Berkshires. Evert Duyckinck came up from New York, this time with his brother George, and many gay outings were planned and carried out—picnics, trips to the mountain top (an overnight excursion) and a masquerade party, given by Mrs. Morewood, who was famous for getting up unusual parties. Boating, fishing and other summer sports were not overlooked. Herman had little time to do more that summer than read the proofs for his forthcoming book and start notes on a new one. *The Whale* was published in London on October 16; and in America it appeared on November 14, with the title page, "Moby Dick; or The

Whale, by Herman Melville. . . . In token of my admiration for his genius, This Book Is Inscribed to NATHANIEL HAWTHORNE."

The dedication came as a surprise to Mr. Hawthorne, who had no idea that his new friend and neighbor was such an ardent admirer, in spite of the fact that Herman's review of *The Mosses* had been glowing with praise. The dedication of a work like *Moby Dick,* so profound, so immense in its scope of thought and vision, was a deeply touching, almost embarrassing tribute to the older writer. He read the work with absorbing interest, neglecting his own manuscript until he had finished the enormous tome —for by the time *Moby Dick* was ended, it had become a triple deck novel, as great in actual length as such a wide-reaching story demanded to be. Hawthorne sat down at once and wrote the author of this strange, wonderful book. When Herman received the letter, he was on the way to the Morewoods'. He read it there, and the words of praise which filled the page filled his heart with more happiness than he had ever thought possible to feel regarding his career. He had to keep his face unmoved at the Morewoods', but a thousand sensations welled up inside him, and he tried to recapture a few of them the next day when he answered the "joy-giving and exultation-breeding" letter, as he called it. It was "the good goddess's bonus over and above what was stipulated for— for not one man in five cycles, who is wise, will expect appreciative recognition from his fellows, or any one of them. . . ."

"I say your appreciation is my glorious gratuity," he went on. "A sense of unspeakable security is in me this moment, on account of your having understood the book. . . . I would sit down and dine with you and all the gods in old Rome's Pantheon. It is a strange feeling—no hopefulness is in it, no despair. Content—that is it; and irresponsibility; but without licentious inclination. I speak now of my profoundest sense of being, not of an incidental feeling. . . ." In a postscript he put: "If the world was entirely made up of Magians, I'll tell you what I should do. I should have a paper-mill established at one end of the house, and so have an endless riband of foolscap rolling in upon my desk; and upon that endless riband I should write a thousand—a million—million thoughts, all under the form of a letter to you." So deep was his gratitude!

To Mrs. Hawthorne, who also praised *Moby Dick,* he wrote: "It really amazed me that you should find any satisfaction in that book. It is true that some *men* have said they were pleased with it, but you are the only *woman* —for as a general thing women have small taste for the sea." But Sophia, he went on to note, saw more than other people and so perhaps was able to read more into *Moby Dick* than most. "I had some vague idea while writing it, that the whole book was susceptible of an allegorical construction," he admitted; but he had not realized how complete an allegory the story was, in part and as a whole, until he received the Hawthornes' letters. It was as if he had written the work that was to become a masterpiece by means of a power outside himself—he hardly knew what he had written until the words were down on the last page. And even then he did not know what he had created.

Sophia's letter had come from West Newton, for the Hawthornes had left the red shanty near Lennox shortly before; and for Herman Melville, the countryside around

Pittsfield no longer shone with a golden light. He began a new book, a novel called *Pierre,* hoping once again to please the public tastes, because *Moby Dick* had received "mixed" reviews and the sales were poor, and his second son had just been born. But he missed his inspiring neighbors, he was exhausted from the tremendous task of *Moby Dick* and he was discouraged because his financial struggles never seemed to end. For fourteen years he lived at Arrowhead, writing, farming, taking time out for another trip abroad and to the Holy Land; then back to writing, watching his children come into the world and grow; seeing three of his sisters marry and move away. Yet none of those years could match the two first happy, productive summers and winters, when Herman Melville and Nathaniel Hawthorne walked through real and imaginary fields, communing with heaven and earth.

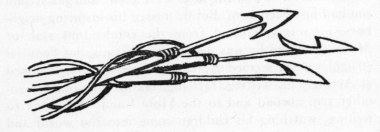

16

THE LAST VOYAGE

Moby Dick was misunderstood—or rather, it was not understood at all by the majority of readers. Even so close a friend as Evert Duyckinck found the character of Captain Ahab [as being] "too long drawn out." Herman, in creating the half-mad master of his whaling vessel, had formed a man with the driving force of Owen Chase, the cruelty of Captain Pease, the inner sickness of Jackson and something of the godlike quality of ancient heroes of mythology. Here was a composite man just as his crew was a combination of the groups of men that circled the globe. Ahab was half-demon, half-god, only in rare instances a "normal" man; and to most readers he was a queer sort of captain, one they found baffling. The whole book was baffling to the general public. Longfellow, who bought one of the first copies to come off the press, noted in his journal that *Moby Dick* was "wild, strange and interesting," but there were not many, even among literary readers, who shared his opinion.

The reviews, both abroad and at home, took the author to task for being too academic in his presentation of whales and whale fishery; for being irreligious and sacrilegious in his story; for too much "morality" and not enough—in short, for everything they did not understand. A few praised the "yarn" so full of color and excitement which carried the reader along swiftly through the whaling scenes; but outside of the Hawthornes and one or two others, no one showed the appreciation of which Herman had dreamed. It was discouraging, but he dared not dwell on his "failure." He had partially regained his popularity with *Redburn* and *White Jacket*. Now *Moby Dick,* on which he had pinned his hopes, was practically another *Mardi* as far as the public was concerned, although it was never intended to be. He would have to try another tack to win back his reputation. Tired as he was from the tremendous exertion of turning out a book like *Moby Dick,* he started a psychological romance called *Pierre* along the lines (he thought) of Hawthorne's romances which had been so successful.

But this sort of novel was not his strong point, and before he was halfway through the plot had become so involved it was unwieldy; yet he stuck to it till the book was completed and tried to be cheerful about its possibilities at publication time. He knew instinctively it was not the artistic success *Moby Dick* had been, but he was counting on the sales appeal to carry him through another year. He was once more doomed to disappointment. *Pierre* was an utter failure. Not a single reviewer had a good word for it, and Herman Melville was advised by more than one of them to go back to the sea for his "material"—there was his great strength.

He decided to try his hand at short pieces, and wrote several magazine stories, articles and essays. (His farm began to prosper, so that he was able to manage without a publisher's advance on a book.) During the next year or so he turned out *Bartleby, the Scrivener. A Story of Wall Street; Cock-a-Doodle-doo;* and a series of sketches, later published in book form on *The Encantadas,* those weird islands in the Pacific where the sailors had found the tortoises. One of his best stories, *Benito Cereno,* was based on a tale he had heard in Chile.

Shortly before his third child, the first girl, Elizabeth, was born, Herman began to write the story of Israel Potter he had planned to do a few years before; and by the time the novel was published, his second daughter, Frances, was born. The four children—Malcolm, Stanwix, "Bessie" and the baby—were healthy and lively; but they were a responsibility, and Herman wondered from month to month whether he could earn enough to support them.

He had not been able to build a "towered house" or even a tower, but he did put up a porch on the north end of Arrowhead, which looked out across the plains and valleys to Saddleback mountain, a beautiful view. He enjoyed sitting or walking on this "piazza," watching the sunset after the day's work was over and thinking about his work. He had written a fanciful story called *The Piazza,* inspired by the distant view of the mountain; and now he proposed publication of a collection of his short stories, to be entitled, *The Piazza Tales*. The volume was so well received by the public that it gave him the assurance he needed for another book and he began *The Confidence Man,* a satire on life and manners in America as seen in the sharp-shooters on the Mississippi river boats.

Both *The Confidence Man* and the job of collecting the short stories were done while he was recovering from an attack of rheumatism which had kept him in bed several weeks. The exposure of his years at sea was beginning to have its effect; if he had many more such attacks, he would be forced to give up the farm. He was worried and nervous. When Judge Shaw offered to finance a trip to Europe and the Holy Land, Herman accepted. His travels took him through Scotland and England to Liverpool, where he had a reunion with Hawthorne, who had been appointed to the United States Consulate there. It was a few days before the two friends could meet, and Herman went to some of the spots he had seen fifteen or sixteen years before on his first voyage. Liverpool was still a dingy dirty seaport, but now the excitement of exploring it was gone. The foggy weather gave him neuralgic pains, and he was glad when Hawthorne sent word to come out to Southport, where the writer and his family were staying. The two men roamed the countryside and talked of the mysteries, the "unknowable" things of life, as they had in Pittsfield. Afterward Hawthorne wrote of his friend and fellow author: "He will never rest until he gets hold of a definite belief. It is strange how he persists—and has persisted ever since I knew him and probably long before—in wandering to and fro over these deserts, as dismal and monotonous as the sand hills amid which we were sitting. He can neither believe, nor be comfortable in his unbelief; and he is too honest and coura-

geous not to try to do one or the other. If he were a religious man, he would be one of the most truly religious
and reverential; he has a very high and noble nature,
and better worth immortality than most of us."

Once again, Herman would have been amazed if he
had read the words of the older writer. He had had the
feeling that the spiritual flame that had lighted their
friendship in the Berkshires was much dimmer in the
sandy hills outside of Liverpool. The reunion was not
what he had expected. Although he saw Hawthorne once
or twice more, he felt that they had not recaptured the
comradeship they had known as neighbors. He parted
from his friend at the end of a day spent touring the town
and cathedral at Chester; when they returned to Liverpool it was raining, and they stood for a few moments on
a dark street corner saying good-by before each went his
way—Herman to the little boardinghouse where he was
staying and Hawthorne to the Consulate.

The following week Herman sailed on the *Egyptian* for
the Mediterranean. The sight of "picturesque" Greece,
Salonika and lofty Mount Olympus brought him out of
his gloominess and stirred his interest in Eastern races,
their culture, art and their different attitude toward life.
When he sailed from Salonika, he was invited to spend
two nights in Cairo, to see the pyramids. They were an
awe-inspiring monument to man's toil, immense and
mysterious; and after he had climbed to the top with his
traveling companion he was overcome with "gradual
nervousness and final giddiness and terror." He would
think of them always as "something vast, indefinite, in-
comprehensible and awful."

From Egypt he went to the Holy Land, where he visited Jerusalem, Jericho, the Dead Sea and Bethlehem.

Every day at dawn he walked outside the walls of Jerusalem, watching the pilgrims who came to pray and the infidels who scorned them. Much later he made use of his observations on the mixture of religion, biblical lore and disbelief in a long poem, *Clarel.*

On the way back he visited Italy—Naples, Rome, the Vatican; museums, churches, palaces; Florence, Venice and Milan came next, then Genoa and on up into Switzerland; and from there to London. Before the voyage home, he visited Oxford and Stratford-on-Avon. Shakespeare's birthplace was one of the places he had long wanted to see. He left for home from Liverpool, where he saw Hawthorne once more, briefly; it was the last time the two were to meet. He sailed on the *City of Manchester,* May 5, 1857, nearly seven months from the time he started his journey.

Judge Shaw welcomed him with a literary dinner in Boston, attended by Oliver Wendell Holmes and Richard Henry Dana among many others. Dr. Holmes was starting a new magazine, *The Atlantic Monthly,* and he asked Herman to be one of the contributors. He was pleased at the request, but he would make no commitments for an article because he received an offer of a lecture tour which would take up most of the following year. He decided to sell Arrowhead so Lizzie and the children would not have to stay on the farm while he was away. The publishing firm that had brought out *The Confidence Man* had folded, so he had lost money on the book in America, and in England it had not sold well. The lectures would pay a high fee, and he needed the money.

The tour, which started in the fall, took him south to Tennessee and up by river boat through Ohio, then back through Pennsylvania to Washington and New York. It was difficult for Herman to speak before an audience, because he was shy, more inclined toward meditation and the written word rather than oral expression of his thoughts; but the lectures were more profitable than unsuccessful books, and he kept on till he had completed his engagements. His listeners found him attractive in appearance, tall, sunburned and sturdy, with a soft, musical voice, but he talked mostly of his recent travels, and the people would have preferred to hear a personal description of his adventures in the South Seas.

He was ill again during the summer, but set out on another tour in the fall. By the time it was over, he had had his fill of speaking in front of an audience, and yet he could not make up his mind on what to do next. He had not found a buyer for Arrowhead, but he was not strong enough to farm it any more. His mother had inherited the family estate at Gansevoort from his Uncle Herman (after whom Herman had been named) and she and Augusta had moved up to the old mansion near Saratoga. Arrowhead was too big for Lizzie to take care of alone. Her father, worried about her and his literary son-in-law, offered to take it off their hands. He would pay off the mortgage and deed the property to Lizzie, so it would belong to them without being a financial burden.

The proposition was a relief to Herman. He had been secretly writing poetry and wanted to perfect his work without the strain of financial worry. He rented a house in Pittsfield for the winter, but when spring came he was restless again. When Tom, who had become captain of the merchant ship *Meteor* arrived home in May, Herman accepted his brother's invitation to make a long voyage with him to the Pacific. Herman was proud of Tom's rise as a sailor. The two, who looked almost like twins since Tom had grown a beard, were perhaps closer than any members of the family. Tom still looked up to Herman for his learning, while Herman had an affectionate regard for the youngest of the Melvilles.

They sailed for the tropics near the end of May. It was a beautiful day, Lizzie had promised to submit the poems for publication and the voyage ahead promised an exciting return to the places Herman had known from his first whaling cruise. The *Meteor* was a fine new clipper ship, and his brother was master of her. He looked forward to sailing the seas of his early years without having to stand watch or sleep in the forecastle.

The sight of the Southern Cross once again made his spine tingle, and one morning he climbed out on the flying jib boom for a "glorious view of the ship" riding the waves full rigged. He enjoyed playing chess with Tom in the cabin at night, and he spent leisurely hours reading Hawthorne's latest book, *The Marble Faun*. The salt air filled his lungs, and the glow of the phosphorescent sea in the darkness of the late hours brought back the wonder and the feeling of mystery he had sensed on his first voyage.

And the awareness of that mystery, as well as the awful power of the "deep" grew upon him as the *Meteor* headed toward Cape Horn. They ran into worse weather than Herman had ever known in rounding the Cape in all his voyages as a sailor. Wind, snow and sleet made the ship roll and pitch, sometimes taking in so much water on deck the sailors were thrown off their feet and washed along the deck; a few nearly went overboard. Herman did not envy them their jobs, and he was full of admiration for the way Tom handled the ship.

When they came within twelve or fifteen miles of "the horrid" sight of Cape Horn, the air grew even colder; sometimes the spray froze as it hit the deck. Darkness came at three in the afternoon. Hailstorms beat upon the sails. Tom was up throughout the night calling orders, trying to bring the *Meteor* and her crew safely through the danger zone. At dawn a young sailor—a Nantucketer about twenty-five years old, to whom Herman had taken a liking—was on the main topsail yard when a terrifying gale of wind tossed him from his precarious perch, hurling him down head first on one of the spars on the deck below.

Herman described the tragedy in a letter to Malcolm: "It was just about daylight; it was blowing a gale of wind; and Uncle Tom ordered the topsails (big sails) to be furled. Whilst the sailors were aloft on one of the yards, the ship rolled and plunged terribly; and it blew with sleet and hail, and was very cold and biting. Well, all at once, Uncle Tom saw something falling through the air, and then heard a thump, and then, looking before him, saw a poor sailor lying dead on the deck. He had fallen from the yard, and was killed instantly.—His shipmates picked him up and carried him under cover. By and by, when time could be spared, the sailmaker sewed up the body in a piece of sailcloth, putting some iron balls— cannon balls—at the foot of it. And, when all was ready, the body was put on a plank, and carried to the ship's side in the presence of all hands. Then Uncle Tom, as Captain, read a prayer out of the prayer-book, and at a given word, the sailors who held the plank tipped it up, and immediately the body slipped into the stormy ocean, and we saw it no more.—Such is the way a poor sailor is buried at sea. This sailor's name was Ray. He had a friend among the crew; and they were both going to California and thought of living there; but you see what happened."

When the sun came out and the skies cleared and the decks dried off on the following day, Herman thought a great deal about the sad fate of young Benjamin Ray and pondered the insolvable riddle of the universe. The blind will of the elements that blew a sailor's life to an early end was a force that would ever be unexplainable to the man who had written of the sea with such accurate word-play that critics ranked him a novelist of the sea along with Daniel Defoe and Richard Henry Dana. Yet he was at a loss to account for the reason behind the fatal accident that had befallen an "honest fellow" like Benjamin Ray. Why should the youthful Nantucketer be struck down, and a foul-mouthed, black-souled sailor like Jackson go on for voyage after voyage, tyrannizing and tormenting his shipmates, while young Ray had shown only friendliness and good-will toward his shipmates?

As the ship plowed northward on the other side of the treacherous Cape and came into the calm waters of the South Pacific, Herman began to put some of his thoughts into poetry. And one moonlight night, when the silver rays streamed through the portholes of the cabin, he read reams of it—"about three cables' length of verses"—to Tom who sat quietly listening, without so much as a single wince, Herman said afterward with a smile. Tom was really a hero to sit through it all, he felt; but to his younger brother the reading was a privilege and a source of deep pleasure.

Tom steered the *Meteor* steadily toward San Francisco, where he planned to pick up cargo bound for Manila and the Orient. The weather was calm, the sea gently

rolling. Herman wrote to his daughter Bessie: "Many sea-
birds have followed the ship day after day. I used to feed
them with crumbs. But now it has got to be warm weather,
the birds have left us. They were about as big as chickens
—they were all over speckled—and they would sometimes, during a calm, keep behind the ship, fluttering
about in the water, with a mighty cackling, and whenever
anything was thrown overboard they would hurry to get
it. But they would never light on the ship. They kept all
the time flying or else resting themselves by floating on
the water like ducks on a pond. These birds have no home,
unless it is some wild rocks in the middle of the ocean.
They never see any orchards, and have a taste of the
apples and cherries, like your gay little friend in Pittsfield, Robin Red Breast, Esq."

One day they spoke a whale ship, and Herman got
into a lifeboat and "sailed over the ocean in it" for an
hour's gam with the whalemen, which brought back memories of his days on the *Lucy Ann*. There were eight or
ten "wild people" aboard, whom the captain had picked
up at Roratonga to help pull in the whaleboat during the
hunt. They reminded Herman of the Maori chieftain and
some of the others he had shipped with, whom he had
described in *Moby Dick*.

Here again, he saw the difference between holding a
gam on the quarter-deck or in the captain's cabin, and
crowding into the forecastle, squatting around on the
bunks swapping stories below deck as he used to do. This
gam, although it was pleasant enough, was not quite so
jolly, so much of a lark as the others had been. Perhaps
he was getting too old and settled. He wrote to Malcolm
about the gam, because he knew his son would be interested, but he suddenly wished he were back in Pittsfield,

telling the children these stories about the voyage instead of writing them across so many thousands of miles.

As usual when he was far away, he felt homesick. He thought of the girls going up over the hill to pick wild strawberries. He drew a sketch of Arrowhead, with himself driving home behind Charlie (the horse) in the carriage and Elizabeth coming out to meet him in the road with the children. By the time the *Meteor* docked at San Francisco, he was ready to return to Pittsfield. Tom was unable to locate a cargo for Manila and would have to wait in San Francisco until something turned up for another destination. Herman decided to sail on the first steamer that would carry him back to his family in the shortest time.

He left the following week for Manzanillo, Acapulco and Panama; he crossed the Isthmus by rail to Aspinwall, where the steamship *North Star* was waiting to take passengers from the west to New York.

Once at home, he was glad to be back, but it was disappointing to learn that neither Elizabeth nor his brother Allan had found a publisher for his poems. Evidently verse was not even as salable as novels. He would have to find something to do besides writing. He thought of Hawthorne's appointment to the Consulate in Liverpool; his friend had tried to secure such a post for Herman at one time, but he was unsuccessful. Now, with the help of Judge Shaw and others, Herman attempted a second time. He went to Washington, armed with letters of recommendation. He met President Lincoln and had an interview with Secretary of State Sumner, who said he would be glad to recommend Herman for the consulship at Geneva, Glasgow or Manchester.

Before the business was settled, a letter came from

Elizabeth calling him home at once; Judge Shaw was dying, and she had to hurry to Boston. Herman left immediately for Pittsfield. And before the matter of a consulship could be settled, the first shot was fired on Fort Sumter and the Civil War had begun.

Judge Shaw left his daughter $15,000, enough to give her and her family a comfortable income. They sold Arrowhead to Allan for use as a summer home and moved back to New York in a house his brother had owned at 104 East Twenty-sixth Street. That address was Herman Melville's home for the next twenty-five years—till the end of his life.

And for twenty of those years he worked as a customs inspector in the United States government; for shortly after they moved to New York, an old acquaintance of his was made collector of customs, and Herman applied for the post of deputy inspector. He received his appointment and began to work at the West Street docks early in December of 1866, a few weeks after *Battle Pieces,* a volume of verse he had written on the Civil War, was published by Harper's. His salary was not much, but it gave him a freedom to write whatever he wished without having to worry about the financial success of his works. *Battle Pieces* received praise, some mild, some enthusiastic; but its sale was small. (The *New York Herald* commented, "For ten years the public has wondered what has become of Melville." People would wonder often during the next ten years about the writer of adventure stories, and then they would forget, but he would not care.)

He wanted only to read, to think and to write as he pleased. As he stood on the West Street docks the first day he started working, on the fifth of December, he was

starting a new life; but to the outside world, it was as if
he were entering a small room and shutting the door on
all that had gone before. While he waited for the ship below to be made fast to its mooring, he stared diligently
at the figures on the rate-sheets he held in his hand, because he was determined to make a success of the steady
position he had at last secured, a post that would release
him from the financial struggles and cares he had always
known. His rather small, but penetrating blue eyes, set
close together under his high brow and heavy shock of
chestnut-colored hair, studied the customs charges with
deep concentration; now and then his right hand rose to
smooth his reddish brown mustache and the full brown
beard which covered the lower part of his face. It was a
raw, misty day, with a fog rising over the river, blotting
out the tops of buildings along the waterfront, and for a
moment he wished to be indoors, snug and dry in the
musty offices of the Customs official.

But as the foghorns sounded in the Narrows, and he
heard the ships pleading for safety going in or out of
the harbor, he lifted his eyes from the page—those small,
round eyes that had so impressed Sophia Hawthorne—
and they seemed to grow larger, more darkly blue. His
face took on the quiet expression of remembrance and of
something strange—dim yet deep—that none of his col-
leagues would ever be able to fathom. He was recalling
the picture of himself as he had started on a new life
aboard the *St. Lawrence* so many years ago on just such
a day as this. It had been early June then and this was
early December, but the weather was the same chilly
dampness, and in a way he felt much the same, only he
was calmer now. Then he had been going off to explore
the outside world; now he was set to explore the inner

world of mind and soul, and nobody could order him about. No critic could tear him to pieces, because he was going to write for himself, and for the few who cared to read his work. . . .

As soon as his duties as deputy inspector had become routine, he began reading in preparation for a long poem he was going to create, based on his experiences in the Holy Land. It was to be a young man's quest for happiness, for belief in God rather than doubt, for the philosophical truths Herman had sought in *Mardi*. But this was to be a religious poem, and while the hero and his companions might examine the values of the world, they did not satirize them. *Mardi* was bitter; the poem, which the author decided to call *Clarel: A Pilgrimage in the Holy Land,* was hopeful and calm. One of the characters, Vine, bore a resemblance to Hawthorne, and was a tribute to his friend who had died suddenly on his return from Liverpool, before Herman had a chance to see him again.

Clarel took several years to write once the years of preparation had ended, and it was 1876 before the volume was published by G. P. Putnam's Sons. The critics were still "puzzled" by Herman Melville; they could not understand why a man who could write adventure stories should occupy himself with deeper themes. Herman had expected this sort of reaction, but once again he had secretly hoped just before publication that he would find understanding from at least one literary mind. He sighed within himself and kept on writing for himself.

He kept on with his job at the West Street docks during the day, and at night he read, wrote a little or visited his old friend, Evert Duyckinck. Tom retired from the sea and was made governor of Sailor's Snug Harbor on Staten Island. He decided to marry, and his big house on the harbor grounds became the family meeting-place for the Melvilles. Herman, especially, was always welcomed, and he enjoyed visiting the place, with its atmosphere of the sea and sailors. He wrote sketches of his old shipmates—Toby, from whom he still heard occasionally; and Jack Chase, and Oliver Russ and some of the others. He wrote poetry or prose as the mood struck him, and he thought about many things.

One of the problems that haunted him was the question of good and evil in the world, the ideas of "morality" that were accepted and upheld by society. All through the years after he returned from the South Seas, he pondered about the decision his cousin Guert Gansevoort had made which brought three sailors to their death. Guert had been changed by the trial, and even though he had distinguished himself in the Civil War, he never again appeared to be at peace with himself. When Herman retired from his job at the customs office in 1886, after twenty years of service, he started to write a novel based on his cousin's story, but told from the point of view of a young sailor.

An article in one of the magazines rehashing the trial and condemning the court-martial, making Lieutenant Gansevoort a thorough villain, spurred on the idea in Herman's mind; and his story showed the struggle of the officers in coming to the verdict of guilty as well as the motives that caused the three sailors to incite "mutiny."

He changed the story, making it more dramatic, and using only one man—the youngest—instead of three. He did not choose the midshipman, Phillip Spencer, but one of the "unknown" conspirators as a basis for the character of his hero. The story was that the youthful sailor had sung out, "God bless the flag!" as he was hanged;

and in Herman's novel, the hero, Billy Budd, a maintop-man known for his angelic goodness, blessed the captain who condemned him to die, even as he walked the plank. In his novel, Herman delved deep into men's souls, into the hidden causes of their actions. *Billy Budd,* like *Moby Dick,* dealt with questions of morality through an absorbing dramatic tale of the sea.

The mariner turned mystic writer did not live to see his last novel published. He became ill shortly after finishing it and died eight months later, in September, 1891. A notice the next day in the *New York Daily Tribune* said of him: "He won considerable fame as an author by the publication of a book in 1847 entitled, *Typee.* . . . This was his best work, although he has since written a number of other stories, which were published more for private than for public circulation." And an item in the *Press* read: "Herman Melville probably reached the height of his fame about 1852, his first novel having been printed about 1847. . . . Of late years Mr. Melville—probably because he had ceased his literary activity—has fallen into a decline, as a result of which his books are now little known. Probably, if the truth were known, even his own generation has long thought him dead, so quiet have been the later years of his life."

Neither Herman Melville, nor the public, realized the great contribution he had made to the world of literature. It was for a later generation to recognize as a writer of one of the masterpieces of all times in *Moby Dick* (and of minor classics in *Billy Budd, White Jacket, Redburn* and the rest), the "young mariner" who was terrified and enchanted by the life of the sea—and who poured out the poetry of his spirit as long as he lived.